LEARNING ENGLISH AS A SECOND LANGUAGE

Workbook — Fourth Level

By
LOIS MORTON

Instructor in English as a Second Language, Cooperative College Center (S.U.N.Y. at Stonybrook), and York College of the City University of New York; formerly of the American Language Program, Columbia University

Illustrated by
ILENE GUTMAN

Special Consultant
CLELIA C. BELFROM

Principal, P.S. 118, Queens, New York; formerly Assistant Director, Bureau for Teaching English as a Second Language, New York City Board of Education

1974
Oceana Publications, Inc.
Dobbs Ferry, New York

First printing: 1974
Second printing: 1978

International Standard Book Number: 0-379-14254-6

This workbook and other titles in the *Learning English as a Second Language Series* are based on an earlier series published by Phoenix Publishing Company, Manila, The Philippines. The authors and publisher gratefully acknowledge the cooperation and permission extended to them by Phoenix and its authors: Fe R. Dacanay, Anita San Juan, Remedios Cayari, Estela Pinga, Dolores T. Dungo and Beatrice Low.

Manufactured in the United States of America

This book belongs to you. Who are you?

Answer these questions about yourself:

What's your name?   _____

What class are you in? _____

What's your room number? _____

What's your teacher's name? _____

More Questions About Yourself

What's your first name? _____

What's your last name? _____

What's your address? _____

What's your apartment number? _____

What city do you live in? _____

What's your telephone number? _____

How old are you? _____

How many brothers do you have? _____

How many sisters do you have? _____

How many older brothers? _____   younger brothers? _____

older sisters? _____   younger sisters? _____

AIM: To identify self

YOUR SCHOOL

Fill in the blank spaces with information about your school.

The name of my school is _____

M _____ is the principal of my school.

M_____ is the nurse.

M_____ is the custodian.

M_____ is my teacher.

M_____ is my gym teacher.

M_____ is my English teacher.

M_____ is my music teacher.

Write the name of each place in the correct column:

auditorium	gymnasium (gym)	music room
cafeteria	office	your classroom
library	nurse's office	principal's office

first floor	second floor
auditorium	_____
_____	_____
_____	_____
_____	_____

CONVERSATION

Who is the principal? (etc.)

Where is the auditorium? (etc.)

Is (_____ *) your teacher? Yes or no. (etc.)

Is the _____ on the (_____) floor? (etc.)

AIM: To learn names and places in the school.

* See guide   2

WHAT'S WRONG WITH THIS CLASSROOM?

Here is a picture of a classroom. There are some things that do not belong in the picture.
Can you tell what they are?

Write some sentences about the picture. Begin each sentence with <u>There is</u> or <u>There are</u>.
Use words from the list below to help you.

<u>two fish</u>   <u>an elephant</u>   <u>a blackboard</u>

<u>a flowerpot</u>   <u>a gun</u>   <u>windows</u>

<u>monkeys</u>   <u>a teacher</u>   <u>books</u>

                                          <u>a guitar</u>

Example: <u>There are 3 windows in the room.</u>

_____

_____

_____

_____

_____

AIM: To reinforce There is and There are; to stimulate conversation; to
write about a picture; to use <u>in</u>, <u>on</u> and <u>under</u>.

3

WHAT ARE THEY DOING?

It is 6:00 P.M. and the Garcia family is at home.

What are they doing?

Add "ing" to each of the words in the list below, and write each word in one of the blank spaces.

cook   sleep   help   play
read   smoke*   watch

1. Mrs. Garcia is _____ .

2. Linda is _____ her mother.

3. Mr. Garcia is _____ the newspaper and _____ a pipe.

4. The cat is _____ on the sofa.

5. Hector and Freddy are _____ television.

6. Freddy is _____ with a toy car.

WHERE ARE THEY?

in the kitchen   in the living room

_____   _____   _____

_____   _____   _____

AIM: To stimulate conversation; to reinforce present continuous
with familiar action words.
*Rule: When a verb ends with "e", take off the "e" when you
add "ing".

WHAT FURNITURE DO YOU SEE IN THE PICTURE?

Look at the picture on Page 4. What pieces of furniture do you see in the Garcia family's apartment? (Name items)

Answer the following questions with Yes, there is or No, there isn't. Write the answers next to the questions.

Is there a stove in the kitchen? _____

Is there a bed in the kitchen? _____

Is there a stove in the living room? _____

Is there a television set in the living room? _____

Is there a rug in the living room? _____

CONVERSATION
Let's talk about your apartment (or house.)

Answer the following questions with Yes, there are, or No, there aren't, Yes, there is, or No, there isn't.

Are there chairs in the kitchen?

Are there pots in the bedroom?

Are there windows in the closet?

Are there chairs in the living room?

Is there a sofa in the bathroom?

Is there a bathtub in the bedroom?

Is there a sink in the living room?

Is there a bookcase in the living room?

Is there a refrigerator in the kitchen?

(Ask each other these questions and then make up other yes and no questions about rooms and furniture.)

COMPLETE THE BLANK SPACES WITH THE MISSING LETTERS

1. s t _ v _	6. t _ l _ v _ s _ _ n
2. s _ n k	7. t _ b l _
3. c h _ _ r	8. r _ g
4. w _ n d _ w	9. r _ f r _ g _ r _ t _ r
5. s _ f _	10. b _ t h t _ b

AIM: To learn names of furniture; to practice is there with article and are there without article; to fill in missing vowels.

5

VOWEL PUZZLES

The five vowels in English are A, E, I, O and U. The letter Y is sometimes a vowel, but
not when it is the first letter of a word. On this page there are some small puzzles. In
each puzzle the vowel is missing. When you fill in the correct vowel, you will have two words,
one across and one down. The words at the left side of the puzzle will tell you what words to
make.

Example: ACROSS: Another word for
         policeman.
     DOWN: Mother cooks rice
         in it.

1. ACROSS: We use if
       for writing.

   DOWN: More than one
       man.

2. ACROSS: The color of
       the sky.

   DOWN: A match will
       do it.

3. ACROSS: You wear it
       on your head.

   DOWN: It says, "Meow."

4. ACROSS: It barks.

    DOWN: Very warm.

5. ACROSS: It flies.
    DOWN: It swims.

6. ACROSS: We use it for
       drinking.

    DOWN: We walk on it.

7. ACROSS: The opposite
       of sad.

   DOWN: Children like
      to eat it.

AIM: To establish what letters are called vowels; to prepare for
    doing a crossword puzzle.
   Note: Point out that letters which are <u>not</u> vowels are called
     <u>consonants</u>.

WHAT DO WE USE THESE THINGS FOR?

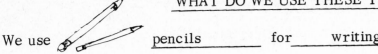

We use ___pencils___ for ___writing___.

From the lists of words below, fill in the blank spaces.
If the word is a thing, write the plural form. (more than one)
If the word is an action, add "ing" to it.

Note: sitting and cutting have 2 Ts.

knife (knives)	towel	drink	wash clothes
chair	needle	dry	keep food cold
dish	bathtub	sew	sweep
glass	refrigerator	sit	cut
ruler	washing machine	eat	
pot		cook	
broom			

We use _____ for _____ .

We use _____ for _____ .

We use _____ for _____ .

We use _____ for _____ .

We use _____ for _____ .

We use _____ for _____ .

We use _____ for _____ .

We use _____ for _____ .

We use _____ for _____ .

We use _____ for _____ .

AIM: To reinforce plurals; to learn irregular plural of knife and when
to add es: to make "ing" forms and use ing after for to show
purpose.

WHAT WERE THEY DOING AT 6:00 YESTERDAY EVENING?

Look at the picture on Page 4. Let's change the time to yesterday evening. What was the Garcia family doing at 6:00?

CONVERSATION

Where was Mrs. Garcia?
Where were Hector and Freddy?
Where were you yesterday evening at 6:00 P.M.?
What was Mrs. Garcia doing?
What was Linda doing?
What was Mr. Garcia doing?
What was the cat doing?
What were Hector and Freddy doing?
What were you doing yesterday evening at 6:00 P.M.?
What was your mother doing?
What was your father doing?

WAS OR WERE
We say: I was, he was, she was, it was; you were, we were, they were

Put the word was or were in the blank space:

1. Hector and Freddy _____watching television.

2. Mr. Garcia _____smoking a pipe.

3. Linda and Mrs. Garcia _____in the kitchen.

4. The cat _____on the sofa.

5. Mrs. Garcia _____cooking.

WRITE ABOUT YOURSELF

What were you doing last night at 7:30 P.M.?

watching television
doing my homework
playing
eating dinner

_____

_____

_____

_____

_____

AIM: To reinforce was and were; to learn the past continuous.

A FIRE DRILL

Every school has fire drills. A fire drill is when you practice what you will do in case of fire. It is important to leave the school building as quickly as possible. You should be quiet, and you shouldn't run or push.

New Words: practice, important, leave, building, quickly, rules.

RULES FOR A FIRE DRILL (Can you say them without looking?)

Stop what you are doing. Listen.

Be quiet.

Get on line.

Follow the teacher.

Don't push.

Don't run.

Don't talk.

CONVERSATION

Answer Yes, you should, or No, you shouldn't.

Should you talk during a fire drill?

Should you listen during a fire drill?

Should you run during a fire drill?

Should you follow the teacher during a fire drill?

Should you be quiet during a fire drill?

Should you push during a fire drill:

AIM: To learn affirmative and negative commands; to reinforce meaning of should and shouldn't.

9

USING THE TELEPHONE IN AN EMERGENCY

Carlos was playing with matches in the kitchen. A fire started in the toaster.

Carlos was frightened. He tried to throw some rags over the fire, but smoke and flames

came through the rags. Carlos ran to the telephone and dialed the operator.

OPERATOR: Operator.
CARLOS: I want to report a fire.
OPERATOR: I'll connect you with the fire department.
FIREMAN: Fire Department.
CARLOS: I want to report a fire.
FIREMAN: Is your mother home? Or your father?
CARLOS: No, nobody is home, except me and my brother.
FIREMAN: Where's the fire? Inside or outside?
CARLOS: In my house, in the kitchen.
FIREMAN: What's your address?
CARLOS: 572 Union Avenue.
FIREMAN: What apartment?
CARLOS: Apartment 4J.
FIREMAN: What number are you calling from?
CARLOS: Mo. 2 - 3591
FIREMAN: We'll send the truck over right away.

CONVERSATION:

Take turns reporting a fire. Give your own address, apartment number and telephone
number. Speak very clearly.

Pronounce these words after your teacher:

	Union	the letter J
	United	danger
What is a rag?	your	jet
	yes	John
What is a rug?	yellow	jello

AIM: To learn how to report a fire; to give vital information slowly
and clearly; to contrast pronunciation of Y and J, and contrast
rag and rug.

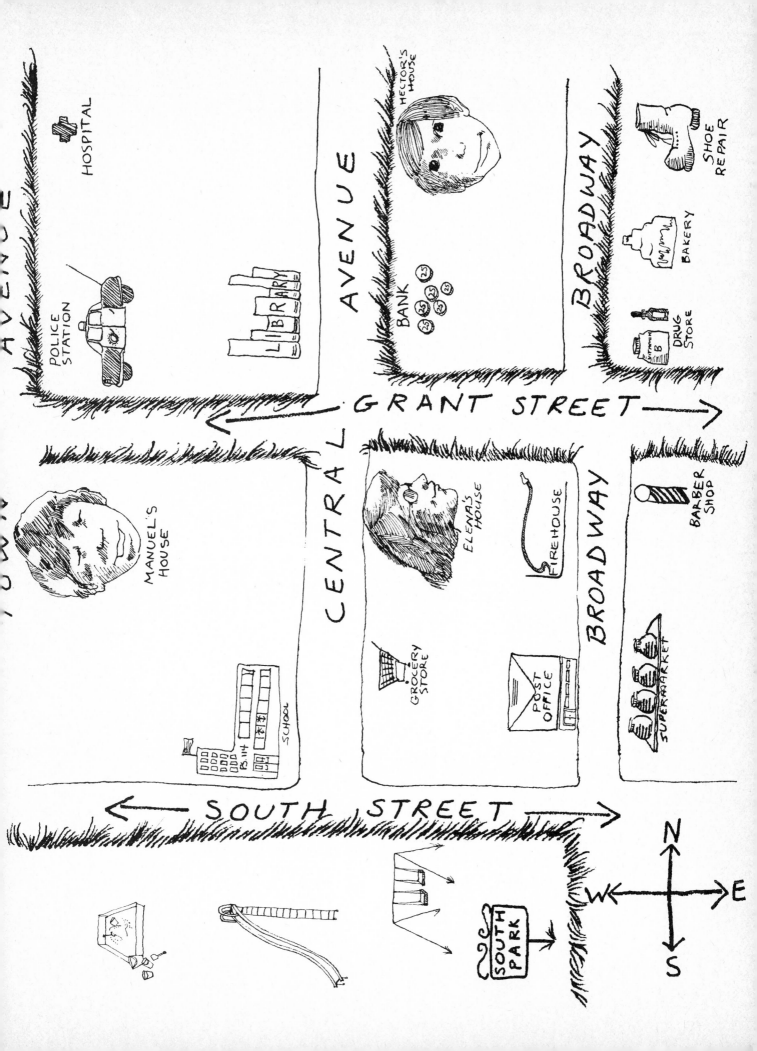

On the lines under each question, write the answer. You will find the answer by looking at the map on the opposite page.

1. Is there a supermarket on Grant Street?

   _____

2. Is there a park across the street from the school?

   _____

3. Is there a playground in the park?

   _____

4. What is across the street from the fire house?

   _____

5. What is between the drug store and the shoe repair shop?

   _____

6. What is next to Hector's house?

   _____

7. What is on the corner of South Street and Central Avenue?

   _____

8. Where is the post office?

   _____

9. What store is on the corner of Broadway and South Street?

   _____

10. What street is east of Central Avenue?

   _____

11. What street is north of South Street?

   _____

12. What street is between Broadway and Town Avenue?

   _____

AIM: To reinforce next to, between;
     To learn across the street from, on the corner of, N.S.E.W.
     To talk about stores and public service agencies.

STORES IN THE NEIGHBORHOOD

Match the words in Column A with the words in Column B.

A   B

shoemaker _____   1. Meat
                                          2. Medicine, toothpaste, band-aids
barber shop _____   3. Bread, cake
                                          4. A haircut, a shave
laundromat _____   5. Torn shoes, broken heels
                                          6. Dirty clothes to wash
drug store _____   7. Milk, butter, eggs, coffee
                                          8. Nails, hammer
hardware store _____   9. Chewing gum, pencils

bakery _____

grocery store _____

butcher _____

candy store _____

TRUE OR FALSE

1. The barber shop sells fish. _____

2. The bakery makes birthday cakes. _____

3. The drug store sells medicine. _____

4. The hardware store sells meat. _____

5. The shoemaker fixes shoes. _____

AIM: To learn names of stores and what is sold in them.

MEASURING FOOD

We measure food in:

<u>pounds</u>   <u>pints</u>   <u>quarts</u>   <u>gallons</u>   <u>dozens</u>

There are 16 ounces in a pound.

There are 16 liquid ounces in a pint.

There are two pints in a quart.

There are four quarts in a gallon.

A dozen is 12.

We buy food in:

| CANS | BOTTLES | CONTAINERS | JARS | BAGS | BOXES |

_____ _____ _____ _____ ____ ____

_____ _____ _____ _____ ____ ____

_____ _____ _____ _____ ____ ____

_____ _____ _____ _____ ____ ____

There are some foods in the following list. Write each food in the column that shows what we take it home in. A can? A bottle? A bag? Some foods can be in more than one column.

Orange juice	coffee	vinegar
tomato soup	milk	oil
sugar	cream	flour
rice	ice cream	eggs
popcorn	strawberry jam	cookies
soda	mustard	potatoes
cereal		

AIM: To learn some units of measure and types of containers;
to recognize names of common foods.

14

BUYING FOOD

Mrs. Vargas usually buys food in the supermarket on Broadway. Sometimes she goes to a small grocery store in the neighborhood. When she needs a lot of food, she goes to the supermarket. When she only needs a few things, she goes to the grocery store. The food is more expensive, but the store is closer to her house, and the grocer is very friendly.

WRITE THE ANSWERS

1. Where does Mrs. Vargas go when she needs a lot of food?

_____

2. Where does Mrs. Vargas go when she only needs a few things?

_____

3. In which store does Mrs. Vargas use a shopping cart?

_____

4. In which store is the food cheaper?

_____

5. Which store is closer to her house?

_____

AIM: To understand reading selection in habitual present;
to understand <u>when</u> <u>clauses</u> and comparisons in context.

CONVERSATION

A DIALOGUE:

IN THE GROCERY STORE   *

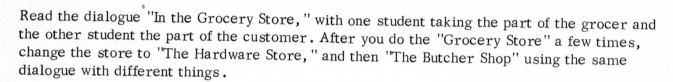

GROCER: Good morning.

CUSTOMER: Good morning. I'd like a quart of milk, half a pound of butter, a loaf of white bread and a jar of mustard.

GROCER: Here you are. That will be $1.45 with tax.
(Customer gives him five-dollar-bill)
Out of five. Thank you, and here's your change; three dollars and fifty-five cents.

CUSTOMER: Thank you.

Read the dialogue "In the Grocery Store," with one student taking the part of the grocer and the other student the part of the customer. After you do the "Grocery Store" a few times, change the store to "The Hardware Store," and then "The Butcher Shop" using the same dialogue with different things.

THE HARDWARE STORE	**THE BUTCHER SHOP**
a flashlight	2 pounds of hamburger meat
2 "C" batteries	2 small chickens, cut in pieces
a box of 1-inch nails	1 pound of frankfurters
3 60-watt light bulbs	
($3.45)	($5.45 out of $10)

SPEAKING CLEARLY

Say these words after your teacher: <u>five</u>   <u>fifty</u>   <u>fifty-five</u>
(Catch your lower lip with your teeth when you say <u>five</u>)
<u>jar</u>   <u>change</u>

AIM: To practice buying food and other items and using numbers in conversation.
* Substitute additional drill items such as:
a bottle of soda
a jar of jam
a head of lettuce
etc.

16

SAVING TIME   (Have children read this several times; act it out)

Eddie Santana walked into the neighborhood grocery store with a long list in his hand.

"What can I do for you?" asked the grocer.

"I want 13 5-pound bags of sugar at 69 cents a bag, 5 quarts of milk at 32 cents a quart, 3 jars of strawberry jam at 49 cents a jar, 25 pounds of rice at 18 cents a pound, 6 loaves of bread at 43 cents a loaf, and 2 heads of lettuce at 39 cents a head. How much is that?"

"That's a big order," said the grocer. "It comes to $19 and 90 cents. Do you have the money with you?"

"No," said Eddie. "I don't want anything today. But thanks a lot. You just did my arithmetic homework!"

AIM: To understand advertisements; to get additional oral
       practice buying food and using numbers.

HOW MUCH?

LOOK AT THE TWO ADS FROM <u>VIC'S DRUG STORE</u> AND THE <u>A & B SUPERMARKET</u> ON

PAGE 17. ANSWER THE FOLLOWING QUESTIONS ABOUT THE ADS. WRITE YOUR

ANSWERS IN NUMBERS.

IN VIC'S SUMMER SALE . . . .

1. How much money can you save on a can of Raid? _____
2. How much money can you save on a pair of sunglasses? _____
3. How much money can you save on a tube of toothpaste? _____
4. How much money can you save on a box of 50 band-aids? _____

AT THE A & B SUPERMARKET . . . . .

5. How much is a dozen eggs? _____
6. How much is a five-pound bag of sugar? _____
7. How much is a gallon of vanilla ice cream? _____
8. What is the difference in price between a 3-pound whole chicken, and a 3-pound chicken cut up?

              A 3-pound chicken costs _____.
              A 3-pound chicken cut in pieces costs _____.
              The difference in price is _____.

DO YOU KNOW . . . .?

9. If one loaf of bread is 43 cents, how much are 3 loaves? _____.
10. If one head of lettuce is 39 cents, how much are 2 heads? _____.
11. If one quart of milk is 35 cents, how much are 4 quarts? _____.
12. If one jar of strawberry jam is 50 cents, how much are 5 jars? _____.

        AIM: To understand abbreviations in advertisements;
              to learn new words <u>save</u> and <u>whole</u>; to do problems
              in subtraction and addition (or multiplication).

DO YOU KNOW HOW MANY?

Write the number in the blank space.

How many seconds are there in a minute? _____

How many minutes are there in an hour? _____

How many hours are there in a day? _____

How many days are there in a week? _____

How many months are there in a year? _____

How many inches are there in a foot? _____

How many feet are there in a yard? _____

How many ounces are there in a pound? _____

How many ounces are there in half a pound? _____

How many ounces are there in a pint? _____

How many pints are there in a quart? _____

How many quarts are there in a gallon? _____

How many pennies are there in a nickel? _____

How many nickels are there in a dime? _____

How many dimes are there in a dollar? _____

How many quarters are there in a dollar? _____

How many pennies are there in a dollar? _____

DO YOU KNOW HOW MUCH?

If you have a quarter, a nickel and a penny, how much money do you have? _____

How much is a dime and two nickels? _____

How much is a quarter and three pennies? _____

AIM: To learn measurements of time, length, weight, money;
To contrast How many and How much; to add.

19

ABBREVIATIONS IN A PUZZLE

Choose from this list of
abbreviations to fill in
the puzzle.

N.Y.C.	min.
Mrs.	sec.
A.M.	hrs.
U.S.A.	gal.
ft.	oz.
in.	lbs.
pt.	T.V.
Mr.	mi.
yds.	qt.
dz.	Dec.

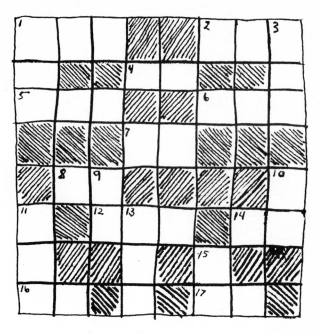

ACROSS

1. minutes
2. gallons
4. dozen
5. seconds
6. hours
7. Mister
8. miles
12. New York City
14. pint
16. morning
17. television

DOWN

1. a married woman
3. pounds
9. inches
10. quart
11. United States of America
12. yards
15. foot

AIM: To learn common abbreviations.

ALPHABETICAL ORDER

Read the letters of the alphabet.

Aa Bb Cc Dd Ee Ff Gg Hh Ii Jj Kk Ll Mm

Nn Oo Pp Qq Rr Ss Tt Uu Vv Ww Xx Yy Zz

How many letters are there in the alphabet?

What is the last letter?

What letter comes before k?

What letter comes after p?

Take turns asking before and after questions. Begin: What letter comes . . . . . .

Here are some words. Copy them in the same order as the letters in the alphabet. The first two are done for you.

fish	chocolate	wall	in	very
sofa	jet	dark	talk	zoo
meat	bread	egg	off	home
arm	go	umbrella	yes	knife
rug	play	nail	x-ray	love

a arm ___   __ ___   __ ___   __ ___

b bread ___   __ ___   __ ___   __ ___

__ ___   __ ___   __ ___   __ ___

__ ___   __ ___   __ ___   __ ___

__ ___   __ ___   __ ___   __ ___

__ ___   __ ___   __ ___   __ ___

__ ___   __ ___   __ ___   __ ___

Riddle: What letter comes after A in the alphabet?   Answer: All of them

AIM: To reinforce the alphabet and arrange words in alphabetical order.

21

THINGS WE DO EVERY MORNING

get up wash your face get dressed eat breakfast
and hands

brush your teeth make your bed go to school

WHAT DOES NANCY DO EVERY MORNING?

Nancy gets up
early every morning.

She washes
her face and
hands.

She gets
dressed.

Then
she eats
breakfast.

After breakfast
she brushes
her teeth.

She makes
her bed.

Then
she walks
to school.

CONVERSATION

What time do you get up every morning?
What times does Nancy get up?
What time do you eat breakfast?
What time does Nancy eat breakfast?
Do you wash your face before you get dressed or after you get dressed?
(etc.)

LET'S WRITE ABOUT NANCY

1. Nancy eats breakfast after <u>she gets dressed</u>   .

2. She brushes her teeth after   .

3. She makes her bed after   .

4. She gets dressed before   .

5. She makes her bed before   .

AIM: To reinforce habitual present with addition of <u>before</u>
and <u>after</u> clauses; to practice third person with <u>s</u>
and <u>es</u>.

TELL ABOUT YOURSELF

CONVERSATION

What time do you get up every morning?

What time do you get up on Saturday mornings? on Sunday mornings?

What do you eat in the morning? (I eat _____ for breakfast.

               I drink _____ in the morning.)

What do you drink?

Do you brush your teeth after breakfast?

Do you make your bed? (Who makes your bed?)

How do you go to school? (Do you walk? Do you go by bus?)

What do you do on Saturday mornings? on Sunday mornings?

NOW, WRITE ABOUT YOURSELF

On the lines below, write some sentences about yourself. Write some of the things you talked about. Tell what you do in the morning. Write about Monday morning or Sunday morning. Use words like:

I get up ...	I don't walk ....
I eat	I don't make my bed ....
I wash	I don't eat ....
I brush	
I watch	

What I Do On _____ Mornings

_____

_____

_____

_____

_____

Something Silly

Nancy learned this silly rhyme from her friends in school. Her friends think it is fun to say it very quickly. Can you say it quickly?

"What's your name?" "Mary Jane."

"Where do you live?" "Down the drain."

"What's your phone number?" "Cucumber."

"What do you eat?" "Pig's feet."

"What do you drink?" "Black ink."

AIM: To talk about habitual activities; to write a short guided composition;
        to memorize five questions the way they are usually pronounced. *see guide.

WHAT DOES HENRY DO EVERY MORNING?

Henry gets up late every morning. He gets dressed quickly, but he doesn't wash his face. He drinks a glass of milk, but he doesn't eat breakfast. He doesn't brush his teeth. He doesn't make his bed. He doesn't walk to school. He runs. He doesn't have time to walk.

Why does Henry run to school?

Because _____ .

DOES AND DOESN'T
Put the word does or doesn't in the blank space in each sentence.

1. Nancy eats breakfast, but Henry _____ .

2. Nancy makes her bed, but Henry _____ .

3. Henry doesn't wash his face, but Nancy _____ .

4. Henry doesn't walk to school, but Nancy _____ .

5. Nancy gets up early, but Henry _____ .

IMPORTANT!
When we talk about (He) or (She), we put an s or es on the action word. But when we say (He doesn't) or (She doesn't) there is no s or es on the action word. We use the original verb form.

EXAMPLES:
Nancy washes her face.
Henry doesn't wash his face.
Nancy has time to walk.
Henry doesn't have time to walk.

READ THE STORY AGAIN, AND UNDERLINE THE CORRECT WORD IN PARENTHESES
IN EACH SENTENCE.

Henry (get up, gets up) late every morning. He (get dressed, gets dressed) quickly, but he doesn't (wash, washes) his face. He (drink, drinks) a glass of milk, but he doesn't (eat, eats) breakfast. He doesn't (brush, brushes) his teeth. He doesn't (make, makes) his bed. He doesn't (walk, walks) to school. He (run, runs). He doesn't (have, has) time to walk.

AIM: To emphasize form of action word in third person negative.

CHOOSE THE CORRECT FORM OF THE WORD IN PARENTHESES:

1. (get up, gets up) Nancy _____ early every morning.

2. (wash, washes) Henry doesn't _____ his face.

3. (get dressed, gets dressed) Henry _____ quickly.

4. (drink, drinks) Henry _____ a glass of milk.

5. (brush, brushes) Nancy _____ her teeth before breakfast.

6. (eat, eats) Henry doesn't _____ breakfast.

7. (make, makes) Nancy _____ her bed before she goes to school.

8. (have, has) Henry doesn't _____ time to walk to school.

LET'S ASK QUESTIONS

Put the word Who, What, Why, When or Where in the blank space at the beginning of each question.

     Example: __Who__ doesn't eat breakfast? Henry.

1. _____ does Nancy do after breakfast? She makes her bed.

2. _____ does Henry run to school? Because he doesn't have time to walk.

3. _____ does Nancy go after she makes her bed? To school.

4. _____ gets up early? Nancy.

5. _____ does Henry get up? Late.

     AIM: To observe difference in third person action words in
           affirmative and negative statements; to reinforce meaning
           of question words.

CHANGING THE TIME

Example: Every day Nancy gets up at 7:30. It's 7:30 now.
    What is Nancy doing? __She's getting up.__

1. Every day Nancy eats breakfast at 8:00. It's 8:00 now.
 What is Nancy doing?_____

2. Every day Nancy walks to school at 8:40. It's 8:40 now.
 What is Nancy doing? _____

3. Every day Henry runs to school at 8:58. It's 8:58 now.
 What is Henry doing?_____

4. Every day you write in your workbook.
 What are you doing now?_____

Note: Look at the spelling of these two words: __running__ __writing__

LET'S ASK QUESTIONS

In the blank space before each question, put the word WHO, WHAT, WHY, WHEN or WHERE.
The answer next to each question will help you.

1. _____does Mr. Vargas work? In an automobile factory.

2. _____is Elena's sister? Anita.

3. _____does the bell ring? At 9:00 every morning.

4. _____is Maria crying? Because she lost her money.

5. _____are you eating? Some ice cream.

6. _____does Hector live? At 225 West 90th Street.

7. _____do you get up? At 7:30.

8. _____gets up early? Nancy.

   AIM: To contrast habitual present and present continuous;
     to reinforce meaning of question words.

WHAT'S WRONG WITH THESE PICTURES?
Put a line under the correct answer.

This is a silly picture because:
  We don't drink from plates.
  We don't drink from glasses.
  We don't drink from cups.

This picture is silly because:
  We can't eat apples.
  We can't eat books.
  We can't read books.

This is a foolish picture because:
  Cars can't sail on water.
  Ships can't sail on water.
  Cars can't go on land.

This picture is silly because:
  We can't write with a pencil.
  We can't eat with a pencil.
  We can't write with a spoon.

This is a silly picture because:
  Pigs don't carry umbrellas.
  Pigs aren't fat.
  Pigs don't sing.

This picture is silly because:
  Fruit doesn't grow on trees.
  Money doesn't grow on trees.
  Leaves don't grow on trees.

AIM: To reinforce negative statements with plural subjects.

OUT OF ORDER

Hector lives at 225 West 90th Street. He lives on the sixth floor. He usually takes the elevator up to his apartment. Today there's a sign on the elevator. The sign says

NOT RUNNING

The elevator is out of order. Hector has to walk up when the elevator is out of order.

Some people can't walk up the stairs. Mr. Ansiano lives on the tenth floor. He's 90 years old. He's too old to walk up the stairs. He has to wait until they fix the elevator.

CONVERSATION

Does Hector live in an apartment?
Do you live in an apartment?
What floor does Hector live on?
What floor do you live on?
What floor does Mr. Ansiano live on?
Why does Hector have to walk up when the elevator is out of order?
Why does Mr. Ansiano have to wait until they fix the elevator?
Why can't Mr. Ansiano walk up the stairs?

WRITE THE ANSWERS

1. Where does Hector live? _____

2. Does Hector usually walk up to the sixth floor? _____

3. Why can't Hector take the elevator today? _____

4. Can Mr. Ansiano walk up to the tenth floor? _____

5. What does Mr. Ansiano have to do? _____

AIM: To practice third person form of <u>have to:</u> to review ordinal numbers.

ORDINAL NUMBERS

We use ordinal numbers for streets, dates, floors of a building, grades in school, and other things that go in order.

I'm always last.

first	sixth	eleventh	sixteenth
second	seventh	twelfth	seventeenth
third	eighth	thirteenth	eighteenth
fourth	ninth	fourteenth	nineteenth
fifth	tenth	fifteenth	twentieth

twenty-first, . . . twenty-fifth, ... thirtieth, etc.

WRITE OUT THE CORRECT NUMBERS IN THE BLANK SPACES:

1. I am in the _____ grade.

2. Christmas is on the twenty-_____ of December.

3. Independence Day is on July _____.

4. My birthday is on the _____ of _____.

5. Mr. Ansiano lives on the _____ floor.

6. Henry lives on the _____ floor.

7. I live on the _____ floor.

8. Next year I will be in the _____ grade.

9. Labor Day is the _____ Monday in September.

10. February is the _____ month of the year.

11. November is the _____ month of the year.

12. December is the _____ month of the year.

AIM: To reinforce pronunciation and spelling of ordinal numbers.

29

Practice asking each other the following questions:

Can you	draw?
	swim?
	read?
Can he	write?
	dance?
Can she	whistle?
	ride a bicycle?
	play the piano?
	play the guitar?
	snap your fingers?
	stand on your head?
	play baseball?
	play basketball?
	roller-skate?
	write script?
	speak Spanish?

NO, I CAN'T.

YES, I CAN

ANOTHER WAY TO ASK THE SAME THING

Ask each other the same questions, but this time say:

Do you know how to	draw?
Does he . .	swim?
Does she . .	etc.

NO, I DON'T.

YES, I DO.

A DIALOGUE:

Mother: Maria, what are you doing with that pencil and paper?

6 year-old Maria: I'm writing a letter to Elena.

Mother: But you don't know how to write!

Maria: That's all right. Elena doesn't know how to read.

AIM: To use "can" and "do you know how to" with appropriate short
answers; to expand vocabulary.

SPEAKING WITH THE RIGHT MELODY

Your voice is like an elevator. It can go up and it can go down. Each language has a "melody"

It is like a song. At certain times the melody goes up. At other times the melody goes down.

Say these two sentences after your teacher. Listen to the melody of each sentence.

A

ARE YOU READY?
The first one goes UP.
Say these with the "A" melody:

ARE YOU LISTENING?

WOULD YOU LIKE A PIECE OF PIE?

DO YOU HAVE ANY BUBBLE GUM?

CAN YOU RIDE A BICYCLE?

Questions with yes or no
answers always go UP.

B

WHAT'S THE MATTER?
The second one goes UP and DOWN.
Say these with the "B" melody:

GOOD MORNING.

I'D LIKE AN APPLE.

WHAT ARE YOU DOING?

HOW ARE YOU? HOW ARE YOU? *

YOU'RE WELCOME.

HAPPY BIRTHDAY.

I HAVE TO GO TO THE DENTIST.

Practice the following dialogue:

CARMEN: Would you like to go to the movies this afternoon?

ROSA: I'd like to, but I can't. I have to go to the dentist.

other places to substitute

the candy store
the basketball game

other things you sometimes have to do

help your mother
do your homework
watch your little brother or sister
go to the doctor.

AIM: To become familiar with major intonation patterns; to practice a
dialogue with can't and have to. Note: See Pages 58 and 93; also 90.

31

TWO KINDS OF HOUSES

Apartment houses are higher than private houses.
Apartment houses are larger than private houses.
Private houses are smaller and lower than apartment houses.
Tall apartment houses have elevators.
Private houses usually don't have elevators.
Many families live in one apartment house.
One or two families live in a private house.
In an apartment house, somebody lives above you,

and somebody lives below you.

If you live on the first floor, the basement is below you.
If you live on the top floor, the roof is above you.

The people who own apartment houses are called LANDLORDS.
(Sometimes the city is the landlord.)

The people who rent apartments are called TENANTS.

If something is out of order in an apartment house, the landlord has to fix it.

If something is out of order in a private house, the people living in the house have to fix it.

AIM: To compare two kinds of houses; to learn new words.

<u>New Words</u>   (Number the words in each column in alphabetical order.)

apartment house	furnace	faucets
private house	boiler	oil
elevator	plumbing	steam
basement	water pipes	garbage
roof	heat	rent
landlord	radiators	pay
tenant		collect

<u>WHAT SHOULD LANDLORDS DO?</u>

Keep the building in good condition.

Fix the elevator when it is out of order.

Fix the plumbing when it is out of order.

Fix the boiler when it is out of order.

Fix the furnace when it is out of order.

Have enough oil to heat the building when
     it's cold.

<u>WHAT SHOULD TENANTS DO?</u>

Keep the apartment clean.

Put the garbage in garbage cans.

Try to be quiet late at night.

Keep the elevator clean.

<u>Draw a line from each word in Column A to the matching word in Column B.</u>

A	B
apartment house	collects rent
private house	goes up and down
landlord	hot water
tenant	steam
plumbing	heat
boiler	pays rent
furnace	water
radiator	large
elevator	small

AIM: To learn and associate new vocabulary; to reinforce <u>should</u>,
      commands (affirmative), and <u>when</u> <u>clauses</u>.

33

<u>CAN'T</u>　　　　　　and　　　　　　<u>HAVE TO</u>

New Words:　<u>electricity</u>, <u>candles</u>, <u>doorbell</u>, <u>ring</u>, <u>knock</u>
　　　　　(Are these words in alphabetical order?)

READ THE FOLLOWING SENTENCES AND THEN FILL IN THE BLANK SPACES WITH
<u>CAN'T</u> OR <u>HAVE TO</u>.

1. There's no electricity.
　　We _____ turn on the lights.
　　We _____ use candles.
　　We _____ watch television.

2. The elevator isn't running.
　　We _____ walk up.
　　We _____ take the elevator.

3. The doorbell isn't working.
　　We _____ ring the bell.
　　we _____ knock on the door.

4. The telephone is out of order.
　　We _____ use the telephone.
　　We _____ go to another telephone.

5. There's no hot water because they are fixing the boiler.
　　We _____ heat the water on the stove.
　　We _____ wash with cold water.

6. There's no water because they are fixing the water pipes.
　　We _____ wash the dishes.
　　We _____ take a bath.
　　We _____ get some water from another building.

7. There's no heat in the building. It's a cold day.
　　We _____ wear our coats.

AIM:　To have further practice using vocabulary of utilities;
　　　　to choose between <u>can't</u> and <u>have to</u> in context.

34

TWO WORDS IN ONE

Can you find two little words in each of the big words?
Put one small word in the blank space in each sentence.

doorbell

1. The _____ is ringing.

2. Open the _____ .

snowball

1. I love to walk in the _____ .

2. The _____ rolled under the car.

somebody

1. Do you know the parts of the _____ ?

2. I need _____ paper.

bedroom

1. We sleep in a _____ .

2. This is the music _____ .

newspaper

1. We write on _____ .

2. We like to hear good _____ .

playground

1. Children like to _____ .

2. The _____ is frozen in the winter.

Riddle: What room is not part of a house?

mailbox

1. Please _____ this letter.

2. I have a _____ of cookies.

sidewalk

1. The sign says "Don't _____"

2. Stay on this _____ of the street.

flowerpot

1. The rose is a _____ .

2. We use a _____ for cooking.

classroom

1. Our _____ has four windows.

2. Our _____ is going on a trip.

bathtub

1. Fill the _____ with water.

2. Please take a _____ .

everywhere

1. We eat lunch _____ day.

2. _____ is your notebook?

Answer: A mushroom.

AIM: To observe how some words are made up of smaller words.

35

UNDERSTANDING SIGNS

DO NOT ENTER

WET PAINT

KEEP OFF THE GRASS

NO PARKING

DANGER

STOP

DON'T WALK

EXIT

ENTRANCE

NO SMOKING

OUT OF ORDER

UP

DOWN

MEN WORKING

DEAD END

SPEED LIMIT

FOR RENT

NURSE'S OFFICE

ONE WAY

SCHOOL . . . DRIVE SLOWLY

PLAY STREET

CLOSED

OPEN

KEEP OUT

WALK

TAXI

BUS STOP

PRINCIPAL'S OFFICE

TEACHERS ONLY

OPEN 24 HOURS

PUSH

KEEP RIGHT

NO RUNNING IN THE HALL

PULL

HELP WANTED

NO VACANCY

SALE- GOING OUT OF BUSINESS

Discussion

Which signs could be on a door?   Put a (✓) next to them.
Which signs could be in the street? Put a (✚) next to them.
Which signs could be in a school? Put an (x) next to them.
Which signs tell you to be careful? Put a (☐) next to them.
Which signs could be in a store? Put a (△) next to them.
Something to do:* Act out a sign without speaking. Can your classmates guess which sign you
            are acting out? Hold up fingers to show how many words there are in the
            sign. Hold up fingers again to show which word you are acting. (First,
            second, etc.)
        AIM: Recognition of common signs; dramatic play.   *See Guide.

HOW MANY SYLLABLES?

What is a syllable?

These words have <u>one</u> syllable.

<u>he</u>   <u>that</u>   <u>cup</u>   <u>hat</u>   <u>burn</u>   <u>dog</u>

Each of the words above has one syllable because there is only one vowel sound. We count one syllable for each <u>vowel sound</u> that we hear. We don't count the consonants.

These words have <u>two</u> syllables because we can hear two vowel sounds.

<u>mother</u>   <u>pencil</u>   <u>silent</u>   <u>doorbell</u>   <u>going</u>   classroom

The next group of words are words that have <u>one</u> syllable. There are two vowels in each word, but one of them is silent. Each of the following words has a SILENT E.

<u>here</u>   <u>make</u>   <u>come</u>   <u>where</u>   <u>time</u>   <u>same</u>   <u>there</u>   <u>hope</u>

<u>How many syllables</u>?

Do these words have <u>one</u> or <u>two</u> syllables? Put the number 1 or 2 in the blank space before each word.

_____father	_____winter	_____present
_____space	_____wanted*	_____shouted*
_____look	_____moving	_____looked*
_____happy	_____hot	_____after
_____home	_____mad**e**	_____went

Now, say the following words to yourself. Then write the number of syllables in the blank space. Will it be 1, 2, 3, or 4?

_____animal	_____Christmas
_____coming	_____intelligent
_____grandmother	_____myself
_____by	_____Saturday
_____dress	_____automobile

AIM: To recognize numbers of syllables in familiar words.
       *see Page 84

SPEAKING CLEARLY

Say these words after your teacher

cooks	flies	washes
eats	swims	brushes
gets	says	uses
makes	goes	teaches
barks	does	fixes
drinks	runs	practices
puts	comes	
takes	lives	
likes	pays	
drops	has	
helps	plays	
looks	cries	
walks	drives	
talks	wears	
collects	leaves	

How many syllables are there in the words in the first column? In the second column? In the third column?

WHICH ONE?

1	2
hat	hot
map	mop
live	leave
hit	heat
cup	cop
sit	seat
fill	feel
pull	pool
full	fool

Your teacher will say one word from column 1 or column 2. Can you hear which word she is saying? Try to hear the difference between the two words. Your teacher will do each pair many times.

AIM: To distinguish between final s, z and ez sounds;
To distinguish between minimal pairs

THE SAME OR DIFFERENT

YOUR TEACHER WILL READ THE FOLLOWING PAIRS OF WORDS.   LISTEN.   DO THE

WORDS IN EACH PAIR RHYME? IF THEY DON'T, PUT AN X ACROSS THE WORDS, LIKE

THIS:

~~poor~~
~~door~~

fish	goes	no	drink
wish	does	do	think
cow	head	keep	some
know	bread	sheep	home
play	wear	cut	top
stay	hear	put	hop
days	make	look	get
says	take	book	yet
roll	cat	food	comb
doll	that	good	bomb
mouth	have	cough	shoe
south	save	enough	toe

AIM: To distinguish pairs of words that rhyme from
      pairs of words that don't rhyme although they
      are spelled the same.

CAN YOU MAKE RHYMES?

Each pair of lines ends in words that rhyme. Look at the first pair, and then finish the others.

The opposite of good is ___bad.___
The opposite of happy is ___sad___.

The opposite of go is ___stop___.
The opposite of bottom is _____.

The opposite of fat is ___thin___.
The opposite of out is _____.

The opposite of young is ___old___.
The opposite of hot is _____.

The opposite of cloudy is ___clear___.
The opposite of far is _____.

The opposite of right is ___wrong___.
The opposite of short is _____.

The opposite of begin is ___end___.
The opposite of enemy is _____.

The opposite of stop is ___go___.
The opposite of yes is _____.

The opposite of push is ___pull___.
The opposite of empty is _____.

AIM: To review familiar opposites; to rhyme words.

Yesterday morning Mr. Garcia got up early.

He washed and shaved

Then he got dressed.

He ate bacon and eggs for breakfast, and drank a cup of coffee.

He brushed his teeth after breakfast.

Then he went to work.

CONVERSATION   "Yes, he did."   No, he didn't."

Did Mr. Garcia get up early yesterday morning?
Did he eat breakfast?
Did he get dressed before he shaved?
Did he brush his teeth after breakfast?

Learn the past forms of these action words:

get - GOT	wash - WASHED	shave - SHAVED
go - WENT	brush - BRUSHED	
eat - ATE		
drink - DRANK		

Write the correct form of the action word in the blank space.

Yesterday morning Mr. Garcia _____ up early. He _____ and

                            get   wash

_____. Then he _____ dressed. He _____ bacon and eggs and _____
  shave   get   eat   drink

a cup of coffee. After breakfast, he _____ his teeth. Then he _____ to work.
                                       brush   go

AIM: To reinforce recognition of past forms; to introduce four irregular forms; to write past forms.

41

TELL ABOUT YOURSELF

CONVERSATION

What time did you get up this morning?
What did you eat for breakfast? What did you drink?
Did you brush your teeth after breakfast?
Did you go to school yesterday?
What did you do in school? (studied, did my work, learned new words)
What did you do after school yesterday afternoon?
Did you watch T.V. yesterday?
What programs did you watch?
What did you eat for dinner (supper) last night? What did you drink?
What time did you go to bed last night?
Did you wash before you went to bed?

NOW, WRITE ABOUT YOURSELF

On the lines below, write some sentences about what you did yesterday. Write some things that you did in the morning, some things that you did in the afternoon, and some things that you did at night (or in the evening.) Here are some words to help you:

got up	washed	watched
ate	brushed	studied
drank	went	learned new words

THINGS I DID YESTERDAY

_____

_____

_____

_____

_____

_____

_____

AIM: To use past forms of action words orally and
in a short guided composition.

A STORY WITH A MORAL

Maria Vargas is six years old. She's in the first grade. Today in school Maria's teacher read this story to the class.

"One day, a mother mouse went for a walk with her children. Suddenly, they saw a cat. The little mice were frightened. The mother mouse looked at the cat.

"Bow! Wow!" barked the mother mouse. The cat thought the mouse was a dog. The cat was frightened, and ran away.

"You see, my children," said the mother mouse, "It's a good idea to learn a second language!"

PUT A LINE UNDER THE BEST ANSWER:

1. The best title (name) for this story is
   a. The Cat and The Dog
   b. It's a Good Idea to Learn a Second Language
   c. A Family of Mice Went for a Walk

2. The mice were frightened because
   a) cats eat mice.
   b) mice eat cats.
   c) mice like cats.

3. The cat ran away because
   a) she saw a dog.
   b) she saw a mouse.
   c) she thought the mouse was a dog.

4. The cat thought the mouse was a dog because
   a) the mouse barked.
   b) the dog barked.
   c) the mouse ran away.

Learn the past forms of these action words.

see - SAW
run - RAN
say - SAID
read - READ
think - THOUGHT

look - LOOKED
bark - BARKED

New Words: suddenly, frightened

AIM: To read and understand a story; to learn more irregular past forms.

43

WRITE THE PAST FORM OF THE WORD YOU SEE UNDER THE LINE:

One day, a mother mouse _____ for a walk with her children. Suddenly,
                              go
they _____ a cat. The little mice _____ frightened. The mother mouse
        see   be
_____ at the cat.
    look

"Bow! Wow!" _____ the mother mouse.
                bark
The cat _____ the mouse _____ a dog. The cat _____ frightened and
          think   be   be
_____ away.
    run

"You see, my children," _____ the mother mouse, "It's a good idea to
                          say
learn a second language!"

SOMETHING TO REMEMBER:
THE WORD "BE"

All these words are forms of the word BE: am, is, are, was, were

ANSWER THESE QUESTIONS:

1. How old is Maria Vargas?

_____

2. What grade is she in?

_____

3. Who went for a walk?

_____

4. Who barked?

_____

5. Who ran away?

_____

AIM: To reinforce more irregular past forms; to
      write answers to comprehension questions.

WHICH WORDS DO NOT BELONG?

Underline the words which do not belong in each box. The first one is done for you.

```
┌─────────────────────────────────────────────────────────────┐
│                          COLORS                             │
│                                                             │
│    red              sky              white                  │
│    purple           black            flower                 │
│    dress            blue             yellow                 │
│    green            home             sandwich               │
└─────────────────────────────────────────────────────────────┘
```

```
┌───────────────────────────────┐   ┌─────────────────────────────────────┐
│          CLOTHING             │   │        PARTS OF THE BODY            │
│  mirror   dress    table      │   │   leg      nose      foot           │
│  shoes    pants    blouse     │   │   arm      ears      paste          │
│  socks    finger   jacket     │   │   father   hand      stomach        │
│  pencil   shirt    sweater    │   │   head     hat       neck           │
└───────────────────────────────┘   └─────────────────────────────────────┘
```

```
┌───────────────────────────────┐   ┌─────────────────────────────────────┐
│           ANIMALS             │   │         TRANSPORTATION              │
│  giraffe  elephant  umbrella  │   │  boat      bicycle     taxi         │
│  book     donkey    mouse     │   │  car       toothpaste  horse        │
│  lion     money     dog       │   │  gasoline  motorcycle  house        │
│  bear     cat       leaf      │   │  jet plane truck       bus          │
└───────────────────────────────┘   └─────────────────────────────────────┘
```

```
┌───────────────────────────────┐   ┌─────────────────────────────────────┐
│      PARTS OF THE HOUSE       │   │            WORKERS                  │
│  stairs   window   wall       │   │  fireman   mechanic    operator     │
│  clock    bus      floor      │   │  policeman school      baker        │
│  evening  kitchen  door       │   │  street    teacher     visitor      │
│  street   chicken  ceiling    │   │  nurse     doctor      butcher      │
└───────────────────────────────┘   └─────────────────────────────────────┘
```

```
┌─────────────────────────────────────────────────────────────┐
│                         HOLIDAYS                            │
│  Christmas        Thanksgiving      June                    │
│  Tuesday          Halloween         Columbus Day            │
│  New Year's Day   December          Labor Day               │
│  October          Friday            Election Day            │
└─────────────────────────────────────────────────────────────┘
```

AIM: To reinforce vocabulary and concept of categories.

45

A GAME WITH WORDS

The words next to each number will tell you what kind of word to write in the blank space.

Example: A day of the week ____Monday____

1. A color _____

2. A month _____ (capital letter)

3. A holiday _____ (capital letter)

4. A food _____

5. A number between 1 and 20 _____

6. A part of the house _____

7. A part of the body _____

8. An animal _____

9. Something in school _____

10. A form of transporation _____

11. A number between 20 and 100 (counting by 10) _____

12. A member of the family _____

TWO WAYS TO PLAY

1. When you teacher calls you, say one of the words that you wrote on the lines above. Somebody in the class has to tell what <u>category</u> the word is in: a color, a month, etc. For example, if you say "January," somebody should say "It's a month."

2. <u>Ten Questions</u>
   When your teacher calls you, say one of the <u>categories</u> on this page. Then the class will try to guess the word that you wrote. For example, if you say, "It's a part of the body," the class will ask questions like, "Is it the <u>nose</u>?" If the class doesn't guess the word in ten questions, you win.

AIM: To reinforce concept of categories and to
practice vocabulary in conversation.

PARTS OF THE BODY
PLAYING "SIMON SAYS"

Can you put the words in the right places? Below is a list of words to choose from. Label the parts of the body.

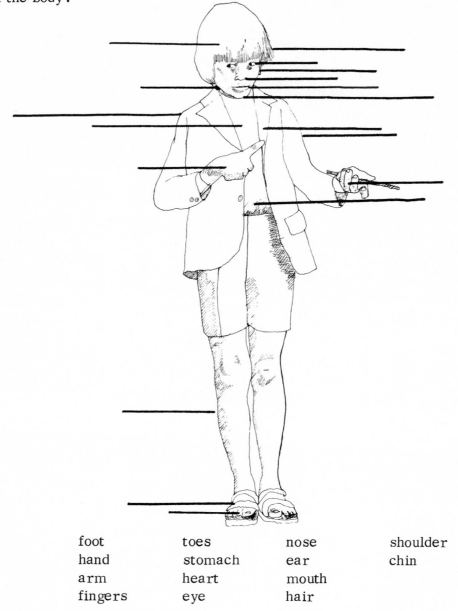

head	foot	toes	nose	shoulder
neck	hand	stomach	ear	chin
chest	arm	heart	mouth	
leg	fingers	eye	hair	

SIMON SAYS

Take turns being Simon. Tell the class what to do.

Simon says, "touch your nose." Simon says, "put your hands on your head." If you don't

say "Simon says", and only say "Touch your ear," the person who touches his ear is out.

Say, "You're out. I didn't say Simon Says."

AIM: To practice commands and parts of the body vocabulary.

A CROSSWORD PUZZLE

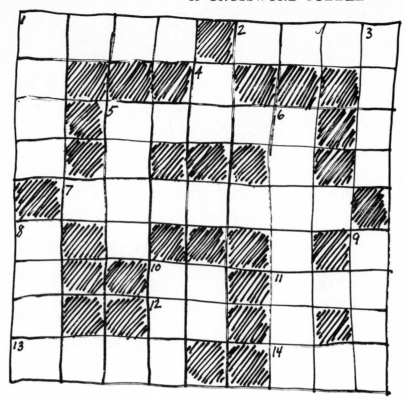

ACROSS

1. You wear a hat on your _____ .

2. Girls wear earrings in their _____ .

5. You wear gloves on your _____ .

7. You touch things with your 10 _____ .

11. You have _____ legs .

12. He lives _____ 225 W. 90th St.

13. You see with your _____ .

14. You wear a _____ on your head .

DOWN

1. You _____ with your ears .

3. You wear a _____ on your foot .

4. You put _____ your coat when you leave school .

5. Comb your _____ .

6. You _____ with your nails .

8. You smell with your _____ .

9. You kick a ball with your _____ .

10. Hector's nose is runny because he he _____ a cold .

AIM: To associate parts of body with functions and certain items of clothing .

MAKING SAFETY POSTERS

Mrs. Green said to her class, "Today we are going to make safety posters." She gave each child a large piece of paper, a ruler and some crayons. She wrote these important sentences on the board:

1. DON'T CROSS THE STREET WHEN THE LIGHT IS RED.

2. DON'T PLAY WITH MATCHES. FIRE IS DANGEROUS.

3. STAY AWAY FROM DRUGS. DRUGS CAN KILL YOU.

4. SMOKING IS BAD FOR YOUR HEALTH.

Then Mrs. Green gave the class the following directions:

Print one of these safety rules across the bottom of your paper.

Try to print the letters in a straight line.

Draw a picture that shows what can happen if people do these things.

Color the picture with your crayons.

The boys and girls drew pictures and colored them. They printed the letters carefully at the bottom of the page. Mrs. Green put some of the posters up on the wall. You can see them on the next page.

New Words: safety, poster, piece, crayons, dangerous, drugs, health, straight, kill,

print, draw, color

Past Forms:

write - WROTE	color - COLORED	print - PRINTED
draw - DREW		
put - PUT		
give - GAVE		

SOMETHING TO DO

Make some safety posters.

CONVERSATION

What are some things you shouldn't do?

AIM: To reinforce affirmative and negative commands; to practice shouldn't; to combine language learning with other activity.

THESE ARE SOME OF THE SAFETY POSTERS THAT MRS. GREEN'S CLASS DREW

DON'T CROSS THE STREET WHEN THE LIGHT IS RED.

DON'T PLAY WITH MATCHES. FIRE IS
DANGEROUS

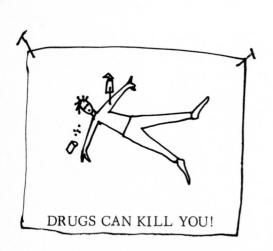

DRUGS CAN KILL YOU!

DON'T SMOKE

AIM: To stimulate ideas for drawing posters; to
understand these four safety slogans.

WHAT ARE YOU GOING TO DO? WHAT ARE YOU DOING NOW? WHAT DID YOU DO?

I'm going to open the door

I'm opening the door.

I opened the door.

She's going to close the window.

She's closing the window.

She closed the window

They're going to buy some bread.

They're buying some bread.

They bought some bread.

WORDS THAT TELL <u>WHEN</u> SOMETHING IS GOING TO HAPPEN:

tomorrow	soon	next year
next week	in ten minutes	tonight
next Monday	next month	

AIM: To contrast future with <u>going to</u>, present continuous, and past.

WHAT IS THE DENTIST GOING TO SAY?

After school today, Henry is going to go home. He's going to eat a few cookies and drink a glass of milk. At 4:00 his mother is going to take him to the dentist. The dentist is going to examine his teeth. Henry hopes that the dentist is going to say, "No cavities!"

CONVERSATION

Is Henry going to go home after school today?

Is he going to eat some apple pie?

Is he going to drink a cup of coffee?

Is his mother going to take him to the dentist at 3:30?

What are you going to do after school today?

ANSWER THESE QUESTIONS. USE "GOING TO" IN YOUR ANSWERS.

1. Where is Henry going to go after school today?

_____

2. What is he going to eat?

_____

3. What is he going to drink?

_____

4. Where is his mother going to take him at 4:00?

_____

5. What is the dentist going to do?

_____

6. What does Henry hope the dentist is going to say?

_____

AIM: To understand a reading passage; to use going to
in oral and written sentences.

CHANGE THE TIME

<u>yesterday</u>   <u>every day</u>   <u>now</u>   <u>tomorrow</u>

Change the action word to fit the time. Look at the example.

Example: Mary walked to school yesterday.

    (every day) <u>Mary walks to school every day.</u>

    (now)   <u>Mary is walking to school now.</u>

    (tomorrow)   <u>Mary is going to walk to school tomorrow.</u>

1. Mother cooks every day.

    (yesterday) _____

    (now)   _____

    (tomorrow) _____

2. I'm helping my teacher now.

    (every day) _____

    (yesterday) _____

    (tomorrow) _____

3. He's going to do his homework tomorrow.

    (every day) _____

    (now)   _____

    (yesterday) _____

4. We speak English every day.

    (yesterday) _____

    (now)   _____

    (tomorrow) _____

AIM: To recognize and contrast four different tenses.

Yesterday afternoon, Mary saw her friend Sally down the street. She called her. "Hi, Sally!" she shouted. Sally heard Mary calling her. She turned around and waved her hand. "Hi, Mary!" she shouted.

SHORT ANSWERS

Did Mary see Sally?*

Did Mary call Sally?

Did Sally hear Mary?

Did Sally answer Mary?

MORE PAST FORMS

see - SAW	call - CALLED	shout - SHOUTED
hear - HEARD	turn - TURNED	
	wave - WAVED	

NOW READ THE STORY AGAIN. UNDERLINE THE CORRECT WORD IN PARENTHESES IN EACH SENTENCE:

Yesterday afternoon, Mary (see, saw) her friend Sally down the street. She (call, called) her. "Hi, Sally!" she (shout, shouted). Sally (hear, heard) Mary calling her. She (turn, turned) around and (wave, waved) her hand. "Hi, Mary!" she (shout, shouted).

Which past form has two syllables?_____

AIM: To use past forms of see, call, hear and answer
with direct object; to contrast pronunciation of d
and ed past endings.
* see guide

54

Yesterday afternoon, John was running down the street. He was in a hurry. He didn't see his friend Hector. Hector shouted, "Hi, John!" John didn't hear him. He didn't answer him. Hector didn't understand why John didn't answer him. He was angry. He didn't speak to John for two days.

What didn't John answer Hector?

Because _____ .

TELLING ABOUT THINGS THAT DIDN'T HAPPEN

You are learning many new forms of words that tell about the past. We use past forms when we talk about what happened yesterday, last week, last year, or five minutes ago. But when we talk about things that didn't happen, the word DIDN'T is the only past form we need. The action word that comes after DIDN'T is <u>not a past form</u>. It is the original verb form.

Look at the examples.

<u>YES</u>	<u>NO</u>
Hector saw John	John didn't see Hector.
Hector spoke to John.	John didn't speak to Hector.

NOW READ THE STORY AGAIN. UNDERLINE THE CORRECT WORD IN PARENTHESES IN EACH SENTENCE.

Yesterday afternoon, John was running down the street. He was in a hurry. He didn't (see, saw) his friend Hector. Hector (shout, shouted), "Hi, John!" John didn't (hear, heard) him. He didn't (answer, answered) him. Hector didn't (understood, understand) why John didn't (answer, answered) him. He was angry. He didn't (speak, spoke) to John for two days.

MORE PAST FORMS

speak - SPOKE understand - UNDERSTOOD answer - ANSWERED

AIM: To show how the negative past works; to stress the use of the original verb form in the negative past.

CHOOSE THE CORRECT FORM OF THE WORDS IN PARENTHESES:

1. (see, saw) Yesterday afternoon Mary _____ Sally.

2. (turn, turned) When Mary called her, Sally _____ around.

3. (shout, shouted) Sally waved her hand and _____ "Hi, Mary!"

4. (hear, heard) John was in a hurry and he didn't _____ Hector.

5. (answer, answered) John didn't _____ Hector.

6. (speak, spoke) Hector spoke to John, but John didn't _____ to Hector.

LET'S ASK SOME QUESTIONS
? ? ? ? ? ? ? ? ? ? ? ? ? ? ? ? ?

Read the example. What happens to the action word
when you ask a question in the past?

Example: Mary saw Sally.   Did Mary see Sally?

1. Mary called Sally.   _____ ?

2. Sally heard Mary.   _____ ?

3. Sally turned around.   _____ ?

4. Hector saw John.   _____ ?

5. Hector spoke to John.   _____ ?

CHANGING THE TIME

Turn back to Page 9 and read RULES FOR A FIRE DRILL.

Mrs. Green's class had a fire drill yesterday. On the lines below write 2 things that they did, and 2 things that they didn't do.

They got on line.	They didn't push.
1. _____	1. _____
2. _____	2. _____

AIM: To contrast affirmative and negative statements in the
past; to form questions with Did.

READ THE FOLLOWING RHYMES. READ THEM A FEW TIMES. CAN YOU SAY ONE OF

THEM FROM MEMORY? TWO? THREE? (One person can do the first and third lines

and another person the second line.) Which sentences use the "A" melody? Which ones

use "B?"

Did you see what I saw?
What did you see?
I saw a big bird flying out of that tree.

Did you hear what I heard?
What did you hear?
I heard a loud noise very close to my ear.

Did you buy what I bought?
What did you buy?
I bought some bananas and blueberry pie.

Did you eat what I ate?
What did you eat?
I ate rice and beans and tomatoes and meat.

Did you drink what I drank?
What did you drink?
I drank lemonade that was tasty and pink.

Did you get what I got?
What did you get?
I got a toy boat and a new TV set.

Did you go where I went?
Where did you go?
I went to the movies and saw a great show.

Did you say what I said?
What did you say?
I said, "How are you? It's a beautiful day!"

AIM: To memorize question pattern in the past with irregular
forms; to stress natural rhythm in verses.

DID YOU LOOK UNDER THE BED?

Hector took out a book from the school library. It was about airplanes. He enjoyed

reading the book very much. A week later, the librarian said to Hector:

> LIBRARIAN: Hector, your library book was due yesterday.
> You can't take out any more books until you
> return the other one.

> HECTOR: O.K., Miss Jones, I'll bring it tomorrow.

Hector went home and looked for the book, but he couldn't find it.
Read the following dialogue between Hector and his mother.

DIALOGUE:

> HECTOR: Mom, I think I lost my library book.
> MRS. GARCIA: Did you look for it?
> HECTOR: I looked everywhere. I can't find it anywhere.
> MRS. GARCIA: Did you look in the living room?
> HECTOR: Yes.
> MRS. GARCIA: Did you look in the kitchen?
> HECTOR: Yes
> MRS. GARCIA: Did you look on top of the refrigerator?
> HECTOR: Yes.
> MRS. GARCIA: Did you look behind the radiators?
> HECTOR: Yes.
> MRS. GARCIA: Did you look in the bathroom?
> HECTOR: Yes. Freddy probably took it. He always
> takes my things!
> MRS. GARCIA: When was the last time you had the book?
> HECTOR: I think I was reading it before I fell asleep.
> MRS. GARCIA: Did you look under the bed?
> HECTOR: No.   Here it is! It was under the bed!

Past forms: lose - LOST   can't - COULDN'T

CONVERSATION

Where did Hector look for his book?
Where did he find it?

Go back to Page 34 and read the exercise aloud with CAN'T and HAVE TO. Change the sentences to the past (yesterday) and use COULDN'T and HAD TO

> AIM: To provide repetition of "Did you . . .?" (See guide.);
> to introduce couldn't as past form; to review vocabulary.

CHOOSING ANSWERS

Find the answer to each question and write the letter in the blank space.

When was the party?	_____	a. in school
How was the party?	_____	b. last Saturday
Where was the party?	_____	c. It was fun.

What did she cook?	_____	a. In the kitchen.
When did she cook?	_____	b. Beans.
Where did she cook?	_____	c. Yesterday.

How did he go downtown?	_____	a. By bus.
Why did he go downtown?	_____	b. This morning.
When did he go downtown?	_____	c. To buy shoes.

What did he sing?	_____	a. at the party.
How did he sing?	_____	b. Very well.
Where did he sing?	_____	c. A Christmas song.

Why did you leave?	_____	a. Home.
Where did you go?	_____	b. Because it was late.
When did you leave?	_____	c. At 11:00.

AIM: To recognize meaning of question words and select
appropriate responses.

WHO DID IT?

It is lunch hour. Mrs. Green is walking under a tree near the school building. Suddenly, she feels some snow hitting her lightly on the head. She sees some children throwing snowballs. Mrs. Green walks over to the children.

(Take turns reading the following dialogue)

MRS. GREEN:	Who threw that snowball?
CHILDREN:	What snowball?
MRS. GREEN:	The one that hit me on the head.
MANUEL:	He threw it.
HECTOR:	What are you talking about? I didn't throw it!
	He threw it.
CARLOS:	I didn't throw anything! He threw it.
MRS. GREEN:	Manuel, did you throw that snowball?
MANUEL:	No, Mrs. Green. He threw it.
HECTOR:	What? I didn't throw it!
MRS. GREEN:	Well, somebody threw it.
ELENA:	Mrs. Green, I saw what happened. Hector threw a snowball at Manuel. The snowball hit the branch of the tree, and some snow fell off the branch and hit you on the head.
MRS. GREEN:	(smiling) Well, then, I guess the tree threw the snowball. But please be more careful next time.

New Words:	snowball, branch
Past Forms:	throw - THREW
	hit - HIT
	fall - FELL

AIM: To practice affirmative, negative and interrogative past with throw; to introduce past question with Who.

MAKING COMPARISONS

Think of a word that will fit in each blank space. The picture before the blank space will help you.

Let's not make any noise! Let's be as quiet as _____.

Henry can help us move the sofa. He's as strong as a _____.

I'm freezing. My hands are as cold as _____.

Everyone loves to look at Maria. She's as pretty as a _____.

Elena is working on something for school. She's as busy as a _____.

I can carry my little sister. She's as light as a _____.

The sun is shining and spring is here. I feel as free as a _____.

We can't use this sugar any more. It's as hard as a _____.

He won't do anything he doesn't want to do.
        He's as stubborn as a _____.

mice	horse	bee	feather	rock
ice	mule	bird	picture	

Riddle: What is as light as air, but the strongest man can't hold it for ten minutes?

Answer: His breath.

AIM: To make comparisons.

Paul is growing.
He is as tall as his mother.

Bob is taller than Paul.

Jack is strong.
He is as strong as his older
brother.

Mr. America is stronger than
Jack.

The mountain is high.
It is as high as the cloud.

An apartment building is
higher than a private house.

Manuel is big.
He is as big as his father.

A truck is bigger than a car.

A straw is thin.
It is as thin as a pencil.

A hair is thinner than a straw.

Spelling Rule: If a word ends in a vowel with one consonant after it, you double the consonant
    when you add "er."
    Look at the example, and then add "er" to the words thin, fat and hot.

Example: big   bigger _____
          1. thin   _____
          2. fat   _____
          3. hot   _____

AIM: To review comparisions with "er", to learn a spelling rule.
    New words: cloud, straw.

62

WHAT'S BIG?   WHAT'S SMALL?

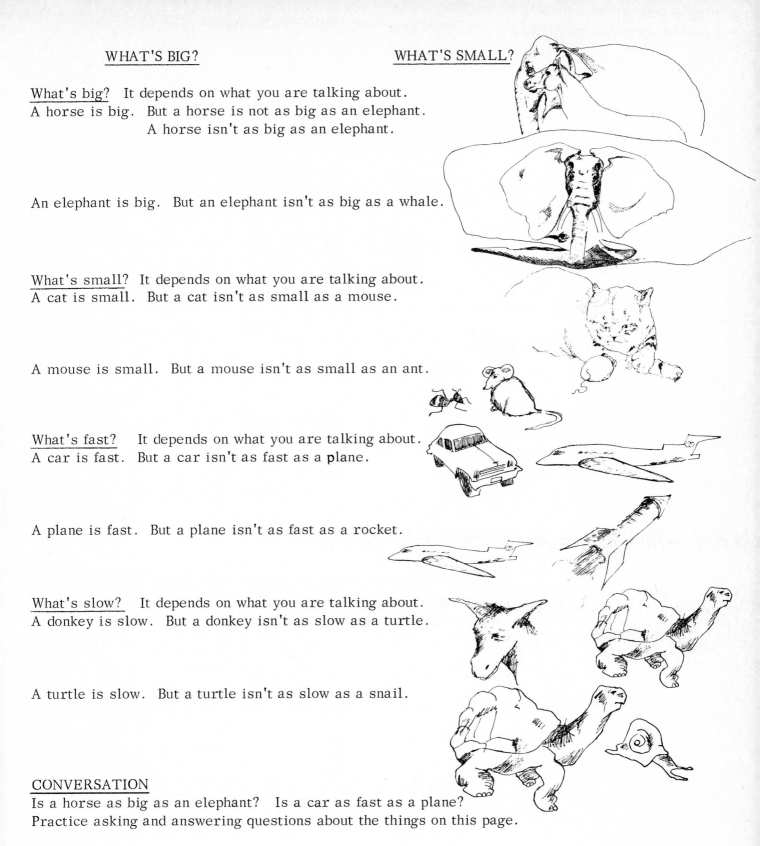

What's big?   It depends on what you are talking about.
A horse is big.   But a horse is not as big as an elephant.
                  A horse isn't as big as an elephant.

An elephant is big.   But an elephant isn't as big as a whale.

What's small? It depends on what you are talking about.
A cat is small.   But a cat isn't as small as a mouse.

A mouse is small.   But a mouse isn't as small as an ant.

What's fast?   It depends on what you are talking about.
A car is fast.   But a car isn't as fast as a plane.

A plane is fast.   But a plane isn't as fast as a rocket.

What's slow?   It depends on what you are talking about.
A donkey is slow.   But a donkey isn't as slow as a turtle.

A turtle is slow.   But a turtle isn't as slow as a snail.

CONVERSATION
Is a horse as big as an elephant?   Is a car as fast as a plane?
Practice asking and answering questions about the things on this page.

        AIM: To understand negative comparisons with as.

63

TELL WHICH ONE ISN'T AS BIG AS, ISN'T AS SMALL AS, ISN'T AS FAST AS, OR ISN'T AS SLOW AS:

Look at the example.

(big) _____A boy isn't as big as a man._____

1. (small)_____

2. (fast)_____

3. (big)_____

4. (slow)_____

5. (small)_____

6. (fast)_____

NOW LET'S COMPARE GROUPS

TELL WHICH ONES AREN'T AS BIG AS, AREN'T AS SMALL AS, AREN'T AS FAST AS, OR AREN'T AS SLOW AS:

Look at the example.

Mice are small. But mice are not as small as ants.

Mice aren't as small as ants.

(fast) _____Cars aren't as fast as trains._____

1. (big)_____

2. (small)_____

3. (fast)_____

4. (slow)_____

5. (fast)_____

AIM: To make negative comparisons with isn't and aren't.

64

WHICH DO YOU LIKE BETTER?
(A Valentine)

Can you say this poem from memory?

I like butter better than cheese.

I like carrots better than peas.

I like hot dogs better than steak.

I like candy better than cake.

I like pizza better than beans.

I like french fries better than greens.

I like chocolate, and pickles too,

But there's nothing that I like better than you.

DISCUSSION

Which do you like better? First talk about the following pairs, and then fill in the sentences

at the bottom of the page.

milk	corn chips	hamburgers	apples
soda	potato chips	hot dogs	oranges

English	books	planes	summer	Saturday
math	movies	trains	winter	Sunday

CHOOSE THREE OF THE PAIRS AND WRITE ABOUT THEM:

Example: I like hot dogs better than hamburgers.

1. _____

2. _____

3. _____

AIM: To memorize a poem; to drill the pattern I
like _____ better than _____ .

65

TWO WAYS TO SAY THE SAME THING

A mouse isn't as big as a cat.
A cat is bigger than a mouse.

Planes aren't as fast as rockets.
Rockets are faster than planes.

COMPARE TWO WAYS:

1. (old)   A boy isn't as old as a man.

A man is older than a boy.

2. (fast) _____

_____

3. (strong) _____

_____

4. (big) _____

_____

5. (heavy) _____

_____

6. (slow) _____

_____

7. (cold) _____

_____

8. (long) _____

_____

AIM: To write comparisons in two ways; to reinforce er suffix.

66

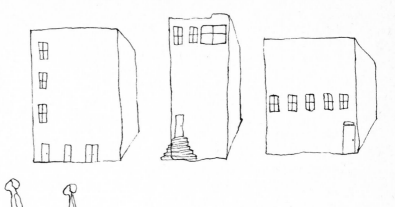

1. Put an X on the narrowest building.

2. Put a circle around the widest window.

3. Put a check (✓) above the thinnest boy.

4. Put an X below the thickest book.

CONVERSATION

What is the best movie you ever saw?

What is the funniest TV show of all the shows that you watch?

What is the shortest month of the year?

What is the biggest animal in the world?

What is the fastest way to travel?

What is the slowest way to travel?

What is the largest state in the United States?

What is the tallest building in New York?

Who is the most beautiful actress in the world? (in your opinion)

Who is the handsomest actor in the world?

What is the most expensive stone in the world?

What is the cheapest thing you can buy in the candy store?

What is the nicest room in your school?

What is the biggest room in your apartment? (house)

Aim: To follow directions; to recognize superlative with est; to hear superlative with most; to talk about familiar things in the superlative. (Additional superlative on Pages 103 and 104.)

THE WINTER FAMILY

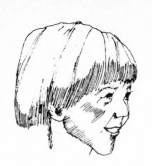

This is Paul Winter. He lives in New York with his family. Mr. and Mrs. Winter are Paul's parents. He has a brother named Henry and a sister named Nancy. Paul's grandmother lives with the Winter family too. Her name is Mrs. Alba. She is Mrs. Winter's mother. Mrs. Alba is Mr. Winter's mother-in-law.

mother	son	brother	husband
father	daughter	sister	wife
parents	grandmother	mother-in-law	children

FILL IN THE BLANK SPACES WITH ONE OF THE WORDS LISTED ABOVE:

1. Henry is Paul's _____.

2. Nancy is Paul's _____.

3. Mr. Winter is Paul's _____.

4. Mrs. Alba is Paul's _____.

5. Paul is Mrs. Winter's _____.

6. Mrs. Winter is Nancy's _____.

7. Mrs. Alba is Mr. Winter's _____.

8. Mr. and Mrs. Winter are Paul's _____.

9. Mrs. Winter is Mrs. Alba's _____.

10. Mr. Winter is Mrs. Winter's _____.

Aim: To learn family relationships; to reinforce possesive with 's with proper nouns.

MAKE SENTENCES WITH THE FOLLOWING WORDS:

Example: Nancy   - daughter   - Mrs. Winter

        <u>Nancy is Mrs. Winter's daughter.</u>

1. Paul   - brother - Nancy

_____

2. Mrs. Alba - grandmother   - Henry

_____

3. Mr. Winter   - father   - Nancy.

_____

4. Paul, Henry and Nancy   - children - Mrs. Winter

_____

NOW, MAKE SENTENCES IN THE SAME WAY, BUT WHERE YOU SEE A CIRCLE
ABOVE THE NAME, CHANGE THAT NAME OR NAMES TO <u>HE</u>, <u>SHE</u> OR <u>THEY</u>

_____

Example:

        <u>Henry</u>   -   son   -   Mr. Winter

        <u>He is Mr. Winter's son.</u>

1.   Nancy   -   daughter   - Mrs. Winter

_____

2. Mr. and Mrs. Winter   -   parents   -   Paul

_____

3. Henry   -   brother   -   Nancy

_____

4. Paul, Henry, and Nancy   -   grandchildren   -   Mrs. Alba

_____

Aim: To use correct word order; to reinforce possessive with <u>'s</u> ;
to substitute subject pronouns for nouns.

69

PUTTING SENTENCES TOGETHER

The words in each group make a sentence. Put number 1 before the part that comes first, number 2 before the part that comes next, and number 3 before the part that comes last.

__3__ to buy some eggs	_____ called his dog
__2__ sent her to the store	_____ the grocer
__1__ Maria's mother	_____ away
_____ a dozen eggs	_____ she was crying
_____ she bought	_____ because
_____ and started to leave the store	_____ he comforted Maria
_____ the grocer's dog	_____ the grocer
_____ of the store	_____ another dozen eggs
_____ was at the door	_____ gave Maria
_____ at Maria	_____ he gave her
_____ and ran after her	_____ candy too
_____ he barked	_____ a piece of
_____ and she dropped	_____ the store
_____ Maria was frightened	_____ she was smiling
_____ the eggs	_____ when Maria left
_____ and broke	
_____ all the eggs	
_____ fell on the sidewalk	

Aim: To put sentences together with correct word order.

MORE PAST FORMS

buy - BOUGHT
send - SENT
fall - FELL

drop - DROPPED

start -- STARTED
comfort - COMFORTED

WRITE THE STORY

Write the sentences from the opposite page on the lines below.
Remember: Begin each sentence with a capital letter and put a period (.) at the end.

1. _____

2. _____

3. _____

4. _____

5. _____

6. _____

7. _____

8. _____

9. _____

10. _____

11. _____

Aim: To practice writing sentences with correct punctuation.

THE VARGAS FAMILY

This is Maria Vargas. She lives in New York with her family. Mr. and Mrs. Vargas are Maria's parents. Maria has a brother named Roberto.

Maria's mother is also Mrs. Alba's daughter. Maria's mother and Paul's mother are sisters. Paul's mother is Maria's aunt. Paul's father is Maria's uncle. Paul is Maria's cousin. Maria, Roberto, Paul, Henry and Nancy are cousins.

aunt	niece	grandchildren
uncle	nephew	grandson
cousin		granddaughter

FILL IN EACH BLANK SPACE WITH ONE OF THE WORDS LISTED ABOVE:

1. Maria is Paul's _____.

2. Mr. Vargas is Paul's _____.

3. Paul is Mr. Vargas' _____.

4. Mrs. Winter is Maria's _____.

5. Maria is Mr. Winter's _____.

6. Roberto is Mr. Winter's _____.

7. Maria is Mrs. Alba's _____.

8. Paul, Henry, Nancy, Maria and Roberto are _____.

AIM: To learn extended family relationships.

MAKE SENTENCES WITH THE FOLLOWING WORDS:

Example: Maria   -   uncle   -   Mr. Winter

     Mr. Winter is Maria's uncle.

1.   Roberto   -   grandmother   -   Mrs. Alba

_____

2.   Nancy   -   cousin   -   Maria

_____

3.   Paul   -   aunt   -   Mrs. Vargas

_____

4.   Maria   -   brother   -   Roberto

_____

NOW, MAKE SENTENCES IN THE SAME WAY, BUT WHERE YOU SEE A CIRCLE ABOVE THE NAME OR NAMES, CHANGE IT TO <u>HIS</u>, <u>HER</u> OR <u>THEIR</u>:*

Example:
    Paul   -   son   -   Mr and Mrs. Winter

    Paul is their son.

1. Mr. Vargas   -   father   -   Maria

_____

2. Mrs. Vargas   -   mother   -   Maria and Roberto

_____

3.   Mrs. Winter   -   aunt   -   Roberto

_____

4.   Mr. Vargas   -   uncle   -   Paul, Henry and Nancy

_____

5.   Mr. Vargas   -   daughter   -   Maria

_____

Aim: To form sentences with correct word order; to substitute possessive
adjectives for nouns with <u>'s.</u>   *see guide

73

MAKING SENTENCES

In this exercise, change <u>all</u> the names. Begin each sentence with HE, SHE, OR THEY.
For words that show belonging, use HIS, HER, or THEIR. Look at the example.

Example: Nancy - daughter - Mr. Winter

<u>She is his daughter.</u>

1. Mrs. Alba - grandmother -Maria and Roberto

_____

2. Paul and Henry - nephews - Mr. Vargas

_____

3. Paul, Henry and Nancy - mother -Mrs. Winter

_____

4. Mr. and Mrs. Winter - parents - Nancy

_____

5. Paul and Henry - sister - Nancy

_____

6. Mr. Vargas - husband - Mrs. Vargas

_____

7. Mr. Winter - uncle - Maria and Roberto

_____

8. Mrs. Winter - wife - Mr. Winter

_____

9. Maria and Roberto - children - Mr. Vargas

_____

10. Maria - cousin - Nancy

_____

Aim: To substitute both subject pronouns and possessive adjectives for nouns;
to reinforce correct word order; to use <u>is</u> and <u>are</u>.

THEY'RE MINE!

A DIALOGUE:

Hector and Carlos are having an argument. It's three o'clock, and the children in Mrs. Green's class are putting on their things and getting ready to go home. Read the dialogue silently, and then take turns acting it out. Your teacher will tell you which parts to play.

CARLOS: Those are my boots!

HECTOR: They're not yours! They're mine!

CARLOS: Give me those boots!

HECTOR: I won't. They're my boots!

MRS. GREEN: Boys, boys, what's the matter?

CARLOS AND HECTOR: He says those are his boots, but they're mine.

MRS. GREEN: Did you look in the closet? Maybe there's another pair of boots on the floor.

ELENA: (looking in the closet) Here's another pair of boots!

MRS. GREEN: Now, we'll see which pair is Hector's and which pair belongs to Carlos.

ELENA: How can you tell? Both pairs are the same color and the same size.

CARLOS: One of my boots has some white paint on the side.

MRS. GREEN: Hector, do your boots have any white paint on the side?

HECTOR: No, they don't.

MRS. GREEN: Then, these are your boots and these are Carlos's.

CARLOS AND HECTOR: Thank you, Mrs. Green.

HECTOR: (putting on his boots) Now I have two left boots.

CARLOS: And I have two right boots.

MRS. GREEN: Oh, goodness! In the future, will you all please write your names inside your boots? Then there won't be any confusion.

(Girls may do the parts as ROSA and CARMEN, and boots can be alternated with shoes , sneakers and gloves.)

Aim: To practice a dialogue with possessive adjectives and pronouns; to introduce will and won't; to contrast left and right.

WHOSE BOOTS ARE THESE?

Example: These boots belong to Carlos.
          They're __his__ boots.
          They're __his.__

1. This notebook belongs to me.
        It's _____ notebook.
        It's _____ .

2. This jacket belongs to him.
        It's _____ jacket.
        It's _____ .

3. This dog belongs to us.
        It's _____ dog.
        It's _____ .

4. These gloves belong to her.
        They're _____ gloves.
        They're _____ .

5. This book belongs to Mrs. Green.
        It's _____ book.
        It's _____ .

6. This pencil belongs to you.
        It's _____ pencil.
        It's _____ .

7. This cat belongs to the Garcia family.   (them)
        It's _____ cat.
        It's _____ .

8. These shoes belong to Hector.
        They're _____ shoes.
        They're _____ .

    Aim: To reinforce possessive pronouns and adjectives; to contrast
        they're and their.

SHORT FORMS

Short forms, or <u>contractions</u> are short ways of saying things.

For example: I'm going.   <u>I'm</u> is short for I am.
You're my friend.   You're is short for You are.
He's my brother.   He's is short for He is.
They aren't here.   Aren't is short for are not.

I'm	we're	isn't
you're	they're	aren't
he's		wasn't
she's		weren't
it's		

Copy each sentence on the line below it. Write the short form for the words which are underlined.

Example: <u>She is</u> my cousin.
                  She's my cousin. _____

1. <u>I am</u> hungry.

_____

2. <u>He is</u> a teacher.

_____

3. <u>You are</u> right.

_____

4. <u>We are</u> not ready.

_____

5. <u>She is</u> not going to the party.

_____

6. <u>It is</u> mine.

_____

7. It <u>is not</u> raining.

_____

8. They have the same last name, but they <u>are not</u> sisters.

_____

9. I called you, but you <u>were not</u> home.

_____

Aim: To recognize contractions for verb "be"

WHAT WILL HAPPEN?

Look at the pictures, and write the word BREAK or TEAR in each blank space.

1.

Hector wrote a note to Elena. Elena and Rita are pulling the paper. If they don't stop, they will _____the paper.

2.

Bill is playing baseball with his friends. If he throws the ball through that window, the window will _____.

3.

The dog is pulling Maria's dress. If he doesn't stop, he'll _____ the dress.

4.

Linda took a book out of the library. If she holds the book like that, the page will _____.

5.

Henry has a dozen eggs in the bag. He is running home. If he drops the bag, the eggs will _____.

6.

The boys are throwing a plate back and forth. If they drop the plate, it will probably _____.

AIM: To understand present-future conditional; to contrast break and tear.

WHAT WILL YOU BE?

aa. a millionnaire
 a. an actor or actress
 b. a nurse
 c. a doctor
 d. a mechanic
 e. an electrician
 f. a secretary
 g. a musician
 h. an airplane pilot
 i. a machine operator
 j. a bus driver
 k. a telephone operator
 l. a mailman
 m. a policeman
 n. a fireman
 o. a soldier
 p. a racing-car driver
 q. a teacher
 r. a baseball player
 s. a singer
 t. a dancer
 u. a construction worker
 v. a plumber
 w. a T.V. repair man
 x. a lawyer
 y. a dentist
 z. a salesclerk

WHO?

(Write the correct letter or letters in
 the blank space.)

_____ helps sick people
_____ plays baseball
_____ puts out fires
_____ teaches children
_____ wears a uniform
_____ sells things in a store
_____ drives a bus
_____ fixes machines
_____ fixes broken T.V. sets
_____ builds houses
_____ delivers mail
_____ runs a machine
_____ fixes electric wires
_____ fixes water pipes
_____ performs in the movies, on the
          stage or on T.V.
_____ carries a gun
_____ flies a plane
_____ helps people on the telephone
_____ has millions of dollars

LET'S BE FORTUNE TELLERS

On a small piece of paper that your teacher will give you, tell the "fortune" of the boy or
girl next to you. Choose one of the professions (jobs) on this page and write:

YOU WILL BE A _____.

Fold the paper and give it to the boy or girl next to you.

Aim: To associate workers with the work they do; to reinforce third person
      present of action word.

WRITING ABOUT THE FUTURE

Look at the "fortune" that your classmate gave you.
(If you don't like it, you can pick another one.)

Let's write some sentences about what we will do in the future.
If you become a _____ , what are some of the things you will do?

What will you do?	Where will you work?	What kind of clothes will you wear?
(Look at the opposite page to get some ideas from the WHO? column.)	in an office in a school in a factory in a hospital outside (out of doors) in a store	a uniform a costume work clothes a white coat regular clothes

Where will you live?

in an apartment
in a house
in the city
outside of the city

MODEL: IF I BECOME A DOCTOR

_____ If I become a doctor, I will work in a hospital. _____

_____ I will help sick people _____

_____ I will wear a white coat. _____

_____ I will live in a big apartment in the city. _____

COMPOSITION: IF I BECOME A ....

_____

_____

_____

_____

_____

Aim: To write a short guided composition; to use the basic form of the
action word after will.

THEY CAME TO THE UNITED STATES SIX MONTHS AGO

The Vargas family lived in Peru last year. Then Mr. and Mrs. Vargas decided to come to the United States. They had relatives living in New York. Mrs. Vargas's older sister came to New York many years ago.

The Vargas family came to the United States six months ago. They came by plane. Roberto and Maria were very excited. They flew in an airplane for the first time.

The plane landed at the airport. The Vargas family took a taxi from the airport to the city. They stayed with their relatives until they found an apartment.

PAST FORMS

come - CAME	live- LIVED	land - LANDED
fly - FLEW	stay - STAYED	decided - DECIDED
take - TOOK		

CONVERSATION

Who came to the U.S. six months ago?
Who came to the U.S. many years ago?
When did you come here?
How did the Vargas family come here?
How did you come here?
Why were Roberto and Maria excited?
Were you excited when you flew in an airplane?
Where did the Vargas family stay when they came to N.Y.?
Where did you stay when you came here?

ANSWERING QUESTIONS

Write the answers.

1. Where do Roberto and Maria live now?

_____

2. Where did they live last year?

_____

3. How did they come here?

_____

4. Where did they stay when they came here?

_____

Aim: To read about and discuss a common experience in the past;
to answer with the correct verb form.

82

MAKING QUESTIONS IN THE PAST

Examples:

They lived in Peru last year. (Did)

_____ Did they live in Peru last year? _____

They lived in Peru last year. (Where)

_____ Where did they live last year? _____

What happens when you use DID at the beginning of a question?

What happens when you use WHERE DID at the beginning of a question?

1.   They came here by plane. (Did)

2. _____ They came here by plane. (How)

3. _____ They came here six months ago. (Did)

4.   They came here six months ago. (When)

_____

WRITING ABOUT YOURSELF

On the lines below, write something about yourself. Here are some questions that you can answer about yourself, but write complete sentences. Begin each sentence with a capital letter and end with a period.

What's your name? Where do you live? Where did you live before?

When did you come here? How did you come here?

Were you excited when you flew in an airplane?

Do you like this city?

_____

_____

_____

_____

_____

Aim: To observe word order in forming questions; to change past form to original form;
to write short guided composition using present and past.

SPEAKING CLEARLY

Say these words after your teacher

T	D	ED
cooked	called	shouted
barked	crawled	started
looked	waved	comforted
walked	shaved	wanted
talked	turned	printed
picked	burned	painted
asked	learned	collected
helped	opened	decided
passed	closed	landed
dropped	lived	
washed	loved	
brushed	showed	
searched	arrived	
watched	rolled	

How many syllables are there in the words in the first column? In the second column?

In the third column?*

WHICH WORD?*

1	2	
wash	watch	Your teacher will say one word from column 1 or column 2. Can you hear which word she is saying? Try to hear the difference between the two words. Your teacher will do each pair many times.
washed	watched	
cash	catch	
work	walk	
would	good	Now you try to say one and the class will guess which word. . . 1 or 2.
when	where	
laugh	love	
safe	save	
trick	treat	
someone	San Juan	

Aim: To distinguish between final t , d, and ed sounds;
To distinguish between minimal and near-minimal pairs.

* see guide

84

CHOOSE THE CORRECT ACTION WORD

Put the correct form in the blank space in each sentence.
Choose from the words at the left.

buy   They are going to _____ a dog.

bought   What is she _____?

buys   Yesterday we _____ a new T.V. set.

buying   Elena's mother always _____food at the supermarket.

eating   I _____too much last night and got a stomach ache.

ate   She _____ sandwiches for lunch every day.

eats   She's _____ a sandwich right now.

eat   He doesn't _____ breakfast in the morning.

breaks   Let go of me! You're _____my arm!

broke   If a dish falls on the floor, it usually _____.

breaking   The eggs fell on the sidewalk and they _____.

flies   I like to _____.

flew   The birds are all _____south for the winter.

flying   Mr. Wilson is a pilot. He _____ a plane.

fly   Two years ago we _____ from Puerto Rico to New York.

tear   The dog pulled Maria's dress with his teeth and it _____.

tearing   Be careful! You'll _____ the page.

tore   "Get the dog away from me." said Maria. "He's _____ my dress!"

AIM: To recognize different tenses and choose the correct form
of the verb.

85

REVIEWING PAST FORMS

Here are some past forms that do not follow any rule.
Do you remember what words they come from?
On the line next to each past form, write a sentence beginning with
DON'T. (Don't use the past form in your sentence.)

ate   Don't eat candy now. _____

tore _____

drank _____

ran _____

threw _____

hit _____

hurt _____

fell _____

broke _____

Write the past form of each word next to the word. Some of the letters are
there. Fill in the missing letters.

go   __w__t_____

think _____ough_____

buy __b____t_____

hear _____a_____

leave _____ft_____

come _____me_____

give _____ve_____

     Aim: To reinforce irregular past forms and negative commands

Yesterday morning Carlos didn't feel well. He had a headache and a sore throat. He didn't want to get up. He wanted to stay in bed.

"I don't feel well, " he said to his mother.

"What's the matter?" she asked?

"I have a headache and my throat hurts when I swallow," said Carlos.

"I'd better take your temperature," said his mother.

She got the thermometer and put it under Carlos's tongue. After three minutes, she took it out and looked at it.

"You have a little fever," she said.

"How much?" asked Carlos.

"Not much - just a little. But I think you'd better stay home today. I'll bring you an aspirin and something hot to drink."

MORE PAST FORMS

feel - FELT	take - TOOK	want - WANTED
know - KNEW		

WHY?
Put a line under the correct answer:

Carlos didn't want to get up because: he was lazy
                                       he felt sick
                                       he didn't want to go to school

Carlos felt sick because: he had a headache and a sore throat
                            he had a stomach ache
                            he had a toothache

Carlos's mother knew he had fever because: she took his temperature
                                            she put her hand on his head
                                            Carlos said he didn't feel well

Aim: To reinforce negative past; to understand because followed
     by reason.

87

CHOOSE THE RIGHT WORD

New Words: temperature, thermometer, tongue, swallow, fever, aspirin

Complete each sentence with a word or words from the list above.

Yesterday morning, Carlos said, "My throat hurts when I _____.

His mother took his _____.   She put the _____ under his _____.

Carlos had a little _____, so his mother gave him an _____. He didn't

got to school.

PUTTING SENTENCES TOGETHER

Sometimes we can put two sentences together by using words like but, or because. In the
following exercise, use the word because to put the sentences together and make one sentence.
Look at the example:

Example: He didn't go to school. He didn't feel well.
He didn't go to school because he didn't feel well.

1. Paul is absent today.   He has a cold.

_____

2. She's crying. She lost her money.

_____

3. His mother took his temperature. He felt sick.

_____

4. I can't go to the movies. I don't have any money.

_____

5. She can't go to the candy store. She has to help her mother.

_____

6. His mother gave him an aspirin. He had a little fever.

_____

Aim: To reinforce vocabulary; to join two sentences with because as the
connecting word.

QUESTIONS AND ANSWERS WITH "WHEN"

Mrs. Rivera's new baby can't talk. He can laugh, he can cry, and he can make noises.

He can't say, "I'm hungry." But he can cry. So, <u>he cries when</u>

<u>he's hungry</u>.

AFTER EACH OF THE FOLLOWING QUESTIONS, UNDERLINE THE CORRECT ANSWER.

Example: When does the baby cry?
           a) when he's happy   b) <u>when he's hungry</u>   c) when he's sleeping

1. When do we drink water?
    a) when we're hungry   b) when we're tired   c) when we're thirsty

2. When does Elena laugh?
    a) when she's angry   b) when she hears a funny joke   c) when she's sad

3. When do you bring an absence note to school?
    a) when you return to school   b) when you're late   c) when you go home

4. When does Mrs. Rivera feed her baby?
    a) when he laughs   b) when he cries   c) when he's sleeping

5. When does Mr. Garcia take off his shoes?
    a) when he comes home   b) when he leaves the house   c) when he goes to work

6. When does Mrs. Garcia turn off the light?
    a) when she gets up   b) when she's cooking   c) when she goes to bed

CONVERSATION

When should you cross the street?
When do you wear a raincoat?
When do you put on your coat? your shoes? gloves?
When do you turn on the light? When do you turn on the TV set?
When do you laugh? When do you cry? When do you get angry?

Riddle: What goes up when rain comes down?

                                   Answer: An umbrella.

Aim: To understand how <u>when clauses</u> are used; to use them in conversation;
        to practice some two-word verbs: <u>put on</u>, <u>take off</u>, <u>turn on</u>, <u>turn off</u>.

SHORT ANSWERS TO QUICK QUESTIONS

Complete the short answer which is correct.

1. Does the sun shine at night?   Yes, ___ _____ .   No, <u>it doesn't</u> .

2. Does the sun set in the west?   Yes, ___ _____ .   No, ___ _____ .

3. Can it rain at night?   Yes, ___ _____ .   No, ___ _____ .

4. Can we count the stars?   Yes, ___ _____ .   No, ___ _____ .

5. Are rats afraid of cats?   Yes, ___ _____ .   No, ___ _____ .

6. Do nurses help doctors?   Yes, ___ _____ .   No, ___ _____ .

7. Is 2/3 bigger than 1/3?   Yes, ___ _____ .   No, ___ _____ .

8. Are you younger than your teacher?   Yes, ___ _____ .   No, ___ _____ .

9. Are all teachers women?   Yes, ___ _____ .   No, ___ _____ .

10. Can a baby write its name?   Yes, ___ _____ .   No, ___ _____ .

11. Do you smile when you're happy? Yes, ___ _____ .   No, ___ _____ .

12. Do you swim when it's cold?   Yes, ___ _____ .   No, ___ _____ .

13. Do you wear boots when it snows? Yes, ___ _____ .   No, ___ _____ .

14. Is a month longer than a week?   Yes, ___ _____ .   No, ___ _____ .

15. Do you laugh when you're sad?   Yes, ___ _____ .   No, ___ _____ .

16. Is your mother's sister your cousin? Yes, ___ _____ .   No, ___ _____ .

17. Is June the sixth month of the year? Yes, ___ _____ .   No, ___ _____ .

18. Are your aunt's children your cousins? Yes, ___ _____ .   No, ___ _____ .

Aim: To understand <u>yes</u> and <u>no</u> questions and associate corresponding short
answers; to reinforce comparisons and <u>when</u> clauses.
Note: Point out that all these questions are said with the "A" up
intonation.

LET'S PLAY THE ANSWER GAME

THE ANSWER IS ....

YES, THEY ARE.

WHAT'S THE QUESTION?

Some possible questions:

Are elephants bigger than horses?　　(Yes, they are.)
Are the windows closed?　　(Yes, they are.)
Are Paul and Maria cousins?　　(Yes, they are.)
Are they studying?　　(Yes, they are.)

You can get other ideas for questions from Pages ___90___ and ___93___ .

USE THESE ANSWERS FOR THE ANSWER GAME:

YES, HE IS.
NO, I WON'T.
YES, SHE DOES.
NO, SHE CAN'T.
YES, THEY DID
YES, I CAN.
NO, HE DOESN'T.
YES, YOU WERE.
YES, I AM.
NO, I CAN'T.

YES, THEY DO.
NO, WE AREN'T.
YES, I DID.
NO, IT ISN'T.
YES, IT IS.
NO, YOU AREN'T.
NO, I WASN'T.
YES, I WAS.
YES, I DO.

and many others!

HOW TO PLAY

1. Your teacher, or one of the students in the class, will say, THE ANSWER
   IS .... and give a short answer.
   Say the answer, write it on the board, or hold it up on a card. The first person
   who can think of a question will raise his hand.

2. Divide the class into two teams. When the "answer-man" (or "answer-girl")
   gives the answer, each team will try to think of a question. Then the members
   of the team will raise their hands. The first team with a correct question will
   win a point.

3. Divide the class into two teams. When the "answer-man" gives the answer,
   each team will have five minutes to think of questions. The team with the most
   questions will win a point.

Aim: To practice word order in questions; to think of questions
beginning with given auxiliary words.

WHICH WORD IS NOT LIKE THE OTHERS?

Put a circle around the word that doesn't belong with the others.

Example:

doctor	lawyer	(circle)	teacher

1. plate — box — cup — dish
2. brother — sister — mother — cat
3. green — large — yellow — purple
4. potato — apple — pineapple — banana
5. twenty — thirteen — high — seven
6. nose — shoes — hands — head
7. book — shirt — pants — jacket
8. piano — flower — bed — chair
9. tall — pretty — fat — work
10. arithmetic — reading — children — writing
11. May — April — December — Tuesday
12. one — third — two — four
13. Maria — Hector — Sally — Elena
14. add — divide — talk — subtract
15. river — book — paper — pencil
16. father — grandfather — grandmother — uncle
17. sun — flower — star — moon
18. Monday — Wednesday — February — Saturday

Aim: To classify words.

FINDING OUT THINGS IN BOOKS

Read the titles of these three books. Which book can give you the answers to the following questions? Write A if it is the first book, B if it is the second book, and C if it is the third book.

A HOW TO TAKE CARE OF PLANTS

B ANIMALS AT THE ZOO

C ALL ABOUT SPACE

_____ What animals eat peanuts?

_____ What are the best months for planting?

_____ Are elephants as big as whales?

_____ Is there life on the moon?

_____ Are roses more delicate than violets?

_____ Do snakes eat grass?

_____ Are elephants bigger than horses?

_____ Who was the first astronaut?

_____ Are mushrooms plants?

_____ What are space-suits made of?

_____ How can we produce bigger oranges?

_____ Are bears more dangerous than lions?

_____ Is the moon a planet?

_____ What do monkeys eat?

_____ Can parrots talk?

_____ How much fuel does a rocket need?

_____ Do plants need water?

_____ Is there life on other planets?

AIM: To classify ideas; to contrast <u>A</u> and <u>B</u> intonation patterns.

READ AND UNDERSTAND

WATER

Underline the correct answer.

All of us need water. People
need water. Plants and animals need
water. Without water we would all die.

This paragraph tells

why we need water.
who needs water.
who will die.

We use water for many things.
We use it for drinking. We use it for
bathing. We use it for cooking. We use
it for washing dirty clothes.

This paragraph tells

what we use water for.
why we wash clothes.
how to be clean.

Water is found in rivers and lakes.
It is found in seas and oceans. It goes up
in the air and becomes clouds. When the
clouds become too heavy, the water falls
on the earth as rain.

This paragraph tells

what rain water is used for.
why there is water.
where water is found.

PUT A CHECK (✓) BEFORE THE WORDS THAT TELL WHAT WE NEED WATER FOR.

_____ for drinking

_____ for washing dishes

_____ for cutting wood

_____ for building a fire

_____ for making a dress

_____ for watering plants

_____ for putting out a fire

_____ for cooking

_____ for washing clothes

_____ for writing letters

_____ for bathing

_____ for drying clothes

_____ for swimming

RIDDLE: What never gets hurt when it falls?   Answer: Rain.

AIM: To get the main idea of a paragraph; to reinforce ing forms
to show what we use things for.

94

ADD OR TAKE AWAY?

Read the following problems. Should you add or take away (subtract) to find the answer?

Put a check next to the word that tells you what to do. Number 1 is done for you.

1. Jack had 7 marbles in his pocket. Two marbles were red and the others were yellow.
    How many marbles were yellow?

    _____ Add   ____✓____ Subtract

2. Maria sent a birthday card to her grandmother. She paid 25 cents for the card and
    8 cents for the stamp. How much money did she spend?

    _____ Add   _____ Subtract

3. John bought a bottle of glue and some crayons for 55 cents. He gave the man in the
    store $1.00. How much change did he get?

    _____ Add   _____ Subtract

4. Ben wants to buy a toy plane for his brother Sam. The toy plane costs $1.50. Ben has
    75 cents. How much money does he need?

    _____ Add   _____ Subtract

5. Bert had 95 rubber bands. He gave his sister 20. How many rubber bands did Bert
    have left?

    _____ Add   _____ Subtract

6. Henry had three packages of gum. His father gave him another one. How many
    packages of gum did Henry have?

    _____ Add   _____ Subtract

7. Victor took a test of 100 questions. He got 67 right. How many did he get wrong?

    _____ Add   _____ Subtract

AIM: To understand problems;
        to distinguish between adding and subtracting;
        to contrast how much and how many.

HOW WILL YOU GET THE ANSWER?

Here are some problems to read. How will you get the answer?
Put a line under the words that tell you how to get the answer. Then write the answer.

1. Roberto is 9 years old. His sister Maria is 4 years old. How many years older is Roberto?

> a. Subtract 9 from 4.
> b. Subtract 4 from 9.

The answer is _____.

2. Tony's mark on the arithmetic test last week was 75. This week his mark was 86. How many points higher was his mark this week?

> a. Subtract 75 from 86.
> b. Add 75 and 86.

The answer is _____.

3. John is 54 inches tall. His brother Bill is 49 inches tall. How many inches taller is John?

> a. Subtract 49 from 54.
> b. Add 49 and 54.

The answer is _____.

4. The temperature in San Juan, Puerto Rico was 80 degrees yesterday. The temperature in New York City was 40 degrees yesterday. How many degrees colder was New York City?

> a. Subtract 80 from 40.
> b. Subtract 40 from 80.

The answer is _____.

5. Victor weighs 95 pounds. Charlie weighs 83 pounds. How many pounds heavier is Victor?

> a. Subtract 83 from 95.
> b. Add 83 and 95.

The answer is _____.

Aim: To understand comparisons of specific quantity.

COMPARING OPPOSITES

Complete these sentences, using your answers from the page before this one.
Use words from the list of opposites on this page.

older	taller	heavier
younger	shorter	lighter
higher	hotter	
lower	colder	

Example: Roberto is __5__ years __older__ than Maria.

         Maria is __5__ years __younger__ than Roberto.

1. Tony's mark was _____ points _____ this week than last week.

    Tony's mark was _____ points _____ last week than this week.

2. John is _____ inches _____ than Bill.

    Bill is _____ inches _____ than John

3. San Juan was _____ degrees _____ than New York yesterday.

    New York was _____ degrees _____ than San Juan yesterday.

4. Victor is _____ pounds _____ than Charlie.

    Charlie is _____ pounds _____ than Victor.

5. (tell about yourself)

    I am _____ years _____ than my brother (or sister).

    My brother (or sister) is _____ years _____ than I am.

       Aim: To use units of measure before comparisons; to reinforce
            opposites.

THEY AREN'T THE SAME

Paul and Henry are brothers, but they are very different from each other. Paul is older than Henry, but Henry is as tall as Paul. Paul is quieter than Henry. Henry is stronger than Paul. Henry is more athletic than Paul, but Paul is more intelligent than Henry. Henry likes to play baseball, football and basketball. Paul likes to do puzzles and read books about science.

YES OR NO

Is Paul as strong as Henry?
Is Henry as old as Paul?
Is Henry as tall as Paul?
Is Paul as athletic as Henry?

FILL THE BLANK SPACE WITH IS OR ISN'T

1. Paul _____ as strong as Henry.
2. Paul _____ as noisy* as Henry.
3. Henry _____ as tall as Paul.
4. Paul _____ as athletic as Henry.

READ THESE TWO SENTENCES:
Henry is more athletic than Paul.
Paul is more intelligent than Henry.

WHEN WE TALK ABOUT THINGS THAT AREN'T THE SAME, SOMETIMES WE USE SHORT WORDS:

tall, old, small, fast

SOMETIMES WE USE LONG WORDS: intelligent, beautiful, important, expensive

WE DON'T ADD ER TO LONG WORDS
WE PUT THE WORD MORE IN FRONT OF THEM.

more intelligent, more important, more expensive
more interesting, more beautiful, more dangerous

How many syllables are there in the word tall? quiet? intelligent?

Aim: To understand comparisons written two ways; To learn when to
use more instead of er.
*see guide.

98

TWO WAYS TO SAY IT

Cars are more expensive than bicycles.
Bicycles are not as expensive as cars.

A candy bar is more expensive than a piece of bubble gum.
A piece of bubble gum isn't as expensive as a candy bar.

YOU DO THE NEXT ONE

_____

_____

DECIDE WHICH FORM TO USE:

Should you add "er" to the word in parentheses, or should you put the word "more" in front of it? Fill in the blank spaces with the correct form.

1. (small) Mice are _____than cats.

2. (expensive) Motorcycles are _____than bicycles.

3. (dangerous) A lion is _____than a mouse.

4. (cheap) Bicycles are _____than cars.

5. (old) Teachers are _____than children.

6. (important) Food is _____than toys.

7. (strong) Henry is _____than Paul.

8. (fast) Planes are _____than trains.

9. (interesting) Sometimes movies are _____than books.

   Sometimes books are _____than movies.

AIM: To show that negative comparisons with <u>not as</u> work the same
      way with long words; to choose between <u>more</u> and <u>er</u> forms.

99

WILL and WON'T

Choose the words that you think should be in the blank space in each sentence. Write the words in the blank space.

Example: If _____it's a nice day_____ tomorrow, we'll go to the park.

        a) it's a nice day
        b) it rains
        c) the weather is bad

1. If _____, he'll go to school tomorrow.
        a) he is sick
        b) he has fever
        c) he feels well

2. If _____, she won't go to school tomorrow.
        a) she feels well
        b) she has a bad cold
        c) she feels better

3. If _____, we will wear boots.
        a) it's a hot day tomorrow
        b) it snows tomorrow
        c) there is no school tomorrow

4. If I see John tomorrow, _____.
        a) I'll tell him what you said.
        b) I'll tell her what you said.
        c) I won't tell her what you said.

5. If it rains tomorrow, _____.
        a) we'll go on a picnic
        b) we won't go to the park
        c) we'll play baseball

6. If the bell rings for a fire drill, _____.
        a) everybody will get in line and leave
           the room
        b) everybody will run out screaming
        c) we won't pay attention to it

Aim: To understand meaning of <u>will</u> and <u>won't</u>;
      to reinforce present-future conditional.

Write the long form for the contraction in each sentence. Below is a list of long forms to choose from.

does not	I will
do not	he will
did not	she will
* cannot	you will
could not	we will
will not	they will

(Note: All the long forms have two words, except one. Which one is it?)

Example: She <u>can't</u> read. _____cannot_____

1. He <u>doesn't</u> want to study. _____

2. <u>Don't</u> do that! _____

3. Were you at the party? We <u>didn't</u> see you. _____

4. He <u>can't</u> whistle. _____

5. I looked everywhere, but I <u>couldn't</u> find it. _____

6. If he is not careful, <u>he'll</u> cut himself. _____

7. If you drop the eggs, <u>they'll</u> break. _____

8. If the weather is nice tomorrow, <u>we'll</u> go to the park. _____

9. I <u>won't</u> be in school tomorrow. _____

10. <u>I'll</u> see you later. _____

11. They <u>don't</u> like bananas. _____

12. We <u>couldn't</u> go swimming because it was cold. _____

13. If you help me, you <u>won't</u> be sorry. _____

14. If you do not help me, <u>you'll</u> be sorry. _____

Aim: To recognize contractions and write their full forms.

*Note: <u>cannot</u> is the only form which is written
as <u>one</u> <u>word</u> in its full form.

IF HE ISN'T CAREFUL,
HE'LL CUT HIMSELF.

IF SHE ISN'T CAREFUL
SHE'LL BURN HERSELF.

IF THEY AREN'T CAREFUL, THEY'LL HURT THEMSELVES

Hector and Linda are going to help their mother in the kitchen. They are going to cut some vegetables and boil some water on the stove. Read the following dialogue and then take turns reading the different parts.

MRS. GARCIA:	Be careful, now, Don't cut yourselves.
HECTOR AND LINDA:	We won't.
LINDA:	Ouch!
HECTOR:	What happened?
LINDA:	I cut myself.
MOTHER:	(running in) What happened to Linda?
HECTOR:	She cut herself.
MRS. GARCIA:	Let me see it. It's all right, but I'd better wash it and put a band-aid on it. Now, please be careful. I'm afraid you're going to hurt yourselves.
HECTOR AND LINDA:	No, no, we won't. We'll be very careful.
HECTOR:	Ouch!
LINDA:	What happened?
HECTOR:	I burned myself.
MRS. GARCIA:	(running in) What happened to Hector?
LINDA:	He burned himself.
MRS. GARCIA:	Let me see it. It's all right, but let cold water run on it. Now, please don't help me any more. I'll finish the supper myself. Get out of the kitchen before you really hurt yourselves.

Aim: To reinforce present-future conditional; to learn reflexive pronouns in two contexts: I cut myself and by myself; to read a fast-moving dialogue.

Nancy, Paul and Henry are sister and brothers. Paul is the oldest of the three. He is also the most intelligent and the most serious. He is the best student in his class. Henry is the strongest and the most atheletic of the three children. He is the best baseball player on the block. Nancy is the youngest of the three. She is also the shortest, but she has the longest hair. Nancy is the funniest person in the family. She loves to tell jokes and riddles. She loves to sing and dance. She is the most talented of the three children.

Discussion

Who is the oldest person in your family?
Who is the most serious person in your family?
Who is the best student in the class?
Who is the youngest person in your family?
Who is the most talented person in your family? Why?
Who is the funniest of all your friends?

Look at the word in parentheses and decide what form to use.
Will you add EST or will you put MOST before the word?

Example: (old) Paul is the   _oldest_____   of the three children.

1. (talented) Nancy is the _____ person in the family.

2. (long)   Nancy has the _____ hair of the three children.

3. (good)* Henry is the _____ baseball player on the block.

4. (serious) Paul is the _____ of the three children.

5. (strong) Henry is the _____ of the three.

AIM: To use superlative forms in conversation; to write them; to contrast est and most

*Note: good is an irregular adjective in comparative and superlative form.

103

READING A T.V. SCHEDULE

T.V. Programs Today

AFTERNOON

3:00	Channel 2	Cartoon: Casper the Friendly Ghost
	Channel 4	Movie: "The Lady and the Monster" A mad scientist creates a monster to destroy the city, but the monster falls in love with the scientist's daughter. (1953)
	5	Bozo the Clown: Comedy Hour
	7	Crime in the City
	13	Sesame Street
3:30	2	Cartoon: Bugs Bunny
	7	What's My Line?
	13	Silent movies

Discussion

How long is the program "Casper the Friendly Ghost?"
Why is there no program on Channel 4 at 3:30?
How long is the program "Bozo the Clown"?
What's on Channel 7 at 3:00?
How old is the movie "The Lady and the Monster?"
What's on Channel 13 at 3:30?
What do you think is the funniest program?
What do you think is the most exciting program?
What do you think is the most serious program?
What do you think is the most educational program?

Speaking Clearly

Say these words after your teacher: * third
Thursday
thirty
thirteen
thirsty

Aim: To learn to read a schedule; to make inferences; to use superlatives
in conversation; to practice /th/ sound in words that sound similar.
*see guide

WORDS THAT TELL US HOW

Example: Mr. Garcia drives a taxi. He drives carefully.
                Which word tells us how Mr. Garcia drives?
                Write the word in the blank space. _____

1. A turtle walks slowly. A rabbit runs quickly.

    Which word tells us how a turtle walks? _____

    Which word tells us how a rabbit runs? _____

2. Mrs. Green doesn't have a loud voice. She speaks softly.

    Which word tells us how Mrs. Green speaks? _____

3. "Boys and girls," said the teacher. "I will be busy for a few minutes. Please work quietly."

    Which word tells us how the teacher told the class to work? _____

4. Bob threw the match carelessly into the waste basket and started a fire.

    Which word tells us how Bob threw the match? _____

5. Harry plays the trumpet well. When he practices, people enjoy listening to him. Sam plays the trumpet badly. When he practices, people close their windows angrily.

    Which word tells us how Harry plays the trumpet? _____

    Which word tells us how Sam plays the trumpet? _____

    Which word tells us how people close their windows? _____

      AIM: To introduce adverbs with ly, and adverb well.

MORE ABOUT WORDS THAT TELL US HOW

We can make new words out of old words.

<u>These are words that you know.</u>   <u>Add LY and you will make these words.</u>

    slow . . . . slowly

    quick. . . . . quickly

    beautiful. . . . . beautifully

    bad . . . . badly

    quiet . . . . quietly

    careful . . . . carefully

    happy . . . . happily

    easy . . . . easily

    soft. . . . . softly

    careless . . . . carelessly

<u>Fill in each blank space with a word that ends in "ly".</u>

    Example: How does a snail move?

        A snail moves __slowly__ .

1. How does a jet plane fly?
   A jet plane flies _____ .

2. Mrs. Green has a soft voice. How does Mrs. Green speak?
   Mrs. Green speaks _____ .

3. We hold our ears when Sam plays the trumpet. How does Sam play?
   Sam plays the trumpet _____ .

4. She looks to the right and the to left when she crosses the street.
   How does she cross the street?
   She crosses the street _____ .

5. The lesson was easy for Elena. How did Elena learn the lesson?
   Elena learned the lesson _____ .

EXCEPTION: We don't add "ly" to the word <u>good</u>. Good changes to <u>well</u>.
    Example: How does Harry play the trumpet?
        Harry plays the trumpet __well__ .

    Aim: To show how adverbs are formed; to point out that <u>good</u> is irregular.

106

SCRAMBLED SENTENCES

On the blank lines, write the sentences in the correct order. Remember to start each sentence with a capital letter and end with a period or question mark.

Example: to morning Nancy walks school every

Nancy walks to school every morning.

1. doesn't breakfast Henry eat

_____

2. see John friend his didn't

_____

3. paint shoe some I left white got my on

_____

4. pencil don't a have I

_____

5. to mother doctor Hector's tomorrow going to take him the is

_____

_____

6. are doing what you?

_____

7. smaller planes are cars than

_____

8. Mr. work Vargas does where?

_____

9. came States the ago they United six to months

_____

10. cut if careful she herself isn't she'll

_____

Aim: To reinforce patterns learned; to arrange words in the correct order.

A DOG SAVED HIS LIFE

Many years ago, in the early 1800s, there was a little boy who lived on a farm. There weren't many children near the farm, and the little boy didn't have many friends. Sometimes he was lonely.

One day, he found a little lost dog with a broken leg. He picked up the little dog carefully and took him home. He took very good care of him, and soon the little dog's leg was better. The dog loved the boy very much, and the boy loved the dog.

One day in the spring, the boy went hunting with his dog. Many hours passed, and they didn't come home. The boy's mother was very worried. The boy's father and some other men went out to look for them. For many hours they searched, but they couldn't find the boy.

New words: lonely *
                hunting
                worried
                searched

ANSWER THE FOLLOWING QUESTIONS:

1. Where did the little boy live?

_____

2. Why didn't he have many friends?

_____

3. Why did he pick up the little dog carefully?

_____

4. Where did the boy and his dog go one day in the spring?

_____

5. Why was the boy's mother worried?

_____

6. Was the boy's father worried? Why?

_____

   Aim: To read and understand a story in the past tense.
         *see guide

108

The men searched for many **h**ours, but they couldn't find the boy and the dog. Suddenly, they heard a dog barking. They ran in the direction of the noise, and found the little dog in front of the entrance to a small cave. He was barking loudly. There was a rock blocking the entrance to the cave. When they rolled the rock away, they found the boy inside the cave. He was tired and frightened, but he was safe.

The boy grew up and became a great sportsman. He was a wrestler, a baseball player and a handball champion. He also became a lawyer. And, one day, he became the sixteenth president of the United States. The boy's name was Abraham Lincoln.

New Words:
cave
wrestler
handball
champion

MATCHING OPPOSITES

Draw a line from each word in column A to the word with the opposite meaning in column B.

Column A	Column B
lost	big
loudly	calm
better	exit
worried	found
entrance	quietly
little	few
many	worse
inside	could
couldn't	outside

Aim: To read and understand a story; to match antonyms.

Put a __T__ in front of each sentence that is true. Put an __F__ in front of each sentence that is false.

_____There were many children near the farm where the little boy lived.

_____He found a little lost dog with a broken leg.

_____He took care of the little dog.

_____The dog loved the boy very much.

_____The boy went hunting with his dog in the spring.

_____The boy and the dog returned home early.

_____The boy's mother was worried because they didn't come home.

_____The boy's father said, "Don't worry, He'll be home soon."

_____The men heard a dog barking.

_____They found the dog behind a tree.

_____They found the dog in front of a small cave.

_____The entrance to the cave was open.

_____The boy was inside the cave.

_____The boy was dead.

_____The boy was frightened.

_____The dog became president of the United States.

Aim: To remember what was in the story.

TIPS FOR TEACHERS

TIPS FOR TEACHERS

Level IV of Learning English as a Second Language follows the basic principle employed in the first three levels of the series: in learning a second language there must be emphasis on hearing, imitation and practice, then reading and writing. New structures and vocabulary should be introduced sequentially, and controlled in order to establish a firm foundation for language learning. As in every kind of learning, there is no substitute for the enthusiasm and interest of the teacher. The Oceana material provides a controlled base from which to operate, endeavoring to present interesting subject matter within which structures may be learned, reviewed, and reviewed again in expanded context.

By the time the student has reached Level IV, he or she should be ready to read most of the material contained in this book. However, a problem frequently encountered is that some students who are quite capable of handling the material orally will not yet have attained the necessary reading skills. The dual tasks of learning to speak a second language, and at the same time to read a language which presents difficulties to its native speakers must be aided by careful selection and organization; at no time should the second language learner be overwhelmed by having to grasp too much material at one time.

To equalize the situation for all the children in the group, it is suggested that the teacher use the following method:

Before beginning a lesson in the workbook, introduce orally and in context those words which may be difficult to read, so that all the students have the opportunity to hear them. Have the words repeated, making sure that they are understood. Then write them on the board and go over their pronunciation, pointing out other words already familiar to the children which may follow a similar pattern.

If the lesson begins with a reading passage, the teacher should read the story first, having the children either listen with their books closed, or follow silently with their books open. Use the conversation questions to check for comprehension. The teacher may then wish to read the passage again, one sentence at a time, having the students repeat, and then have them take turns reading aloud. If there is dialogue in the story, have the group alternate taking parts, and concentrate on the conversational elements in the lesson. After reading, they will be ready to do the written exercises. (Those exercises which were done orally may later be used to provide additional writing practice.)

Note: Since drill is of paramount importance in acquiring firm language habits, the teacher should provide additional pattern drills wherever the material lends itself. For example, the conversation on page 6 between clerk and customer gives an excellent opportunity to substitute additional drill items such as a bottle of soda, a jar of jam, a head of lettuce, etc. There are also a number of games which once learned can be used again: Simple Simon, on page 47; Charades, on page 36; The Answer Game, on page 91; Categories, on page 46; and Minimal Pairs, on pages 38 and 84.

TEACHER'S TABLE OF CONTENTS

TEACHER'S TABLE OF CONTENTS